LA SANTÍSIMA TRINIDAD CHURCH, ARROYO SECO

All proceeds
are paid to the
Holy Trinity Parish's
Restoration Fund

OUT OF TIME

OUT OF TIME
James C. Bull
Wolff Publishing Works ~ Taos

Library of Congress Cataloging-in-Publication Data

Bull, James C.
Out Of Time / James C. Bull

ISBN 0-9669299-0-X
0 1 2 3 4 5 6 7 8 9

Published and printed in the United States of America

FIRST EDITION

December 1998

Book & cover designed by Terry R. Wolff
Painting on cover "Arroyo Seco"
by Ed Sandoval, Studio de Colors

WOLFF PUBLISHING WORKS
P.O.Box 1583
El Prado / Taos
New Mexico
87529

www.taoswolf.com/wolfpub

DEDICATED TO
THE VILLAGERS OF ARROYO SECO, NEW MEXICO
PAST AND PRESENT

This book was made possible through the generosity of many people. Contributors and editors to the text, photographs, and artwork included Holy Trinity Parish, Father Vincent Chávez, Larry Torres, Lisa Mower, Terry Wolff, and Pablo Quintana. Editors of specific text portions: Arsenio and Kathy Córdova, Palemón Martínez, Barbara Waters and Trudy Healy. Connie Bull and Sachiko Nagata assisted in proofreading. Wendy Boyd helped in formatting and maintaining continuity.

We are very grateful for the financial contributions of the following Sponsors and Supporters.

CO-SPONSORS
ALBERT SIMMS, ESQ. OF TAOS
PEOPLES BANK OF TAOS
ALL ABOUT TAOS OF ARROYO SECO
STUDIO DE COLORES
ED SANDOVAL & ANN HUSTON
ED & TRUDY HEALY
DONALD AND JOYCE RUMSFELD
FIRST STATE BANK OF TAOS

SUPPORTERS
ABE'S CANTINA & GROCERY
FRANK WATERS FOUNDATION
PIÑON INVESTMENTS OF ARROYO SECO
FRANK SECKLER
TAOS BOOK SHOP
MOBY DICKENS BOOK SHOP
LA VIEJA LOCA
LISA MOWER
CID'S FOOD MARKET
ANNABEL'S STRICTLY BY ACCIDENT
CASA FRESEN
EDWIN J. SMART
TAOS MOUNTAIN BED & BREAKFAST
JULIAN AND FAB TORREZ
DENNIS GARCIA- PONTIFICAL COLLEGE
SALSA DEL SALTO BED & BREAKFAST
COTTONWOOD BED & BREAKFAST

LA IGLESIA DE LA SANTÍSIMA TRINIDAD DE ARROYO SECO, N. M., CIRCA EARLY 1900'S
Larry Torres Archives, Photographer Unknown

PROCESIÓN ALREDEDOR DE LA IGLESIA VIEJA EN ARROYO SECO, CIRCA 1940'S
Larry Torres Archives, Photographer Unknown

CONTENTS

PORQUE ESTAMOS JUNTOS

It was 1952. I often rode south from Denver with my grandfather in his new green DeSoto to Albuquerque along the narrow two-lane ancestor of Interstate-25. We always drove west over La Veta Pass and stopped at Fort Garland long enough to wander around the real frontier stockade built in 1858. That was our special tradition. Then we headed due south to San Luis pausing for lunch on a concrete table built under red willows which had been planted during the depression.

The snow-covered Sangre de Cristo Range on the east was the source of common grazing and timber for the settlers. Fourteen thousand-foot peaks guarded the few passes to the plains and they provided security from uninvited incursions. The town of San Luis functions as the Costilla county seat. It was organized in 1851 when it was still part of the Territory of New Mexico. Today the town's newly constructed pathway to the Stations of the Cross and the new church on the mesa draws visitors from all parts - even across the Sangres.

Further south we crossed the Colorado and New Mexico border at the village of Costilla - which is east of Ute Mountain. It took more than an hour to drive from Costilla to Taos in the 50's. The very narrow road passed through Questa, an old town that has managed to survive on molybdenum buried in its nearby mountain. Deer frequently claimed the right of way in the Carson National Forest. Finally we arrived in Taos six or seven hours after having left Denver. Our family still takes this route to Arroyo Seco except that we turn at Arroyo Hondo and wind carefully up the hill. The trip now lasts a little over 4 hours depending on weather. My grandfather has been gone for thirty years but I suspect that he is still on the trail. The trappers used to call the route The Taos Trail.

I vividly remember driving into Taos on old Highway 3 with its tree-lined roadbed. Livestock, grazing behind the fence-line on both sides of the road, stopped eating to watch as we passed. My grandfather showed me Kit Carson's grave, the Taos Pueblo and the Plaza in town. I took pictures with a small box camera, which are still in my files. Taos'

roads were constructed of dirt, dust and maybe a little gravel in those days and far fewer people and buildings existed. The fancy houses in Las Colonias were sage and space. Now, some of the names are new, truck styles have evolved, and, of course, the main road is paved. Many of the trees along the road are gone.

My wife, Connie, also started visiting Taos in the 50's and skied *Al's Run* at the Taos Ski Valley in the 60's. This run still has the reputation as having one of the most challenging vertical drops in the Rockies. Her family used the Ratón Pass route. So, in 1970 we decided to take *her* trail. We motored through Cimmaron and the old railroad town of Colfax with its rattlesnake filled Pullman Car and the falling-down hotel - which since collapsed. We carefully snaked through the canyon following Highway 64 in the dark. The next day we drove to Arroyo Seco and up El Salto Road. Time's eye plays tricks. Seco looks very much now as I remember it 28 years ago but I know it isn't.

Year after year we would come back to Northern New Mexico. Our three daughters spent many days and nights at The Sagebrush Inn or in El Rincon. Rowena Martínez engaged us with stories of her deceased husband, the influential artist and trader, Ralph Myers. The girls watched videos at Rowena's B & B while the parents were enjoying *sopapillas* at Roberto's. We stayed at the Quail Ridge Inn and received tennis lessons from Kurt, Ted and Yogesh. At the Kachina Lodge we listened to the drums in the evening by the flaming fire pit and jumped into the cold swimming pool at the El Pueblo Lodge directly across the road.

At my suggestion, the three sisters painted rocks from the creek at an A-frame in Ranchitos as a new art form. Then they decided to sell the enhanced stones at a craft fair in Colorado. We gave most of these *Pop Rocks* away for Christmas. Another year our family waded through spring mud at a Bed and Breakfast in Talpa whose owners unfortunately lost their drum factory in a fire the next year. We camped at Chaco Canyon and Aztec, and visited Bandelier National Monument when it was still permissible to stay at the old Frijoles Canyon Lodge.

1994 was special. The family bought a home in Arroyo Seco after a long wait. The previous Thanksgiving had been spent in a nearby house rented for the holiday. Cornish game hen replaced the turkey dinner that year - they were smaller and quicker to roast. We are nearly half way between the Taos Plaza and the Ski Valley. I can ride my bike almost anytime and we can walk the Rim Road toward Cuchilla del Medio in the evening. The adobes in our house were fabricated from the clay of the retaining wall from an old stock pond where the homesite is now located. A nearby acequia lined with chokecherry bushes and wild apple trees follows the Rim Road. Bear tracks headed for fruit trees follow the wet acequia bed. Our *horno* faces El Salto, Lucero Peak and its waterfalls. Fields of alfalfa abut the ground and the Hondo Valley is north.

The following year, after a memorable party downtown and especially happy post-fiesta rejoicing at the Sagebrush, we decided our next project should be to restore a vintage 1952 GMC pickup that needed just a little work. The motor did start, as I recall, and it would stop on occasion. The truck deserved to get back on the road and 1952 celebrated the year our families first visited the area. Three years later the truck is Chinese red with black trim, has a refurbished flatbed and the cab draws humming birds and butterflies during the summer. July 4, 1998 marked her entry into the Third Annual Arroyo Seco Independence Day Parade. Twelve children rode on the decorated flatbed throwing candy to spectators along the way.

In late spring, 1995, I rode my bicycle into the plaza in Arroyo Seco on the way to buy breakfast burritos at Abe's. Volunteers were cleaning the area around the Old Church, mixing, framing and drying adobes, and clearing the roof of deteriorated shingles. Palemón Martínez stopped directing the front loader. He kindly offered me a brief tour of the Old Church. I was shown the hand painted altar screen (reredos) located behind the simple altar. He explained its history and what had to be done to restore the 1834 building. One of the guys on the roof yelled, Come on up and help!

Having grown up near Denver, I knew *notadamnthing* about making adobes although I did have a video that described how to build a *horno*.[1] The video had been purchased at Hacienda de los Martínez during a fall Rendezvous. I replied, "Later." I mentioned that I could do some research and could write a little. And so an idea for the story of the Old Church and its village that could be used to help pay for restoration and maintenance evolved into a substitute for *roofing duties*.

I learned that there were others who had accomplished substantial work on similar projects and had written or conducted detailed research on Arroyo Seco's long history. I discussed my idea with various (but not all) of these academics and villagers before committing my time to this new effort. The general subject matter was not new but I hoped to approach it from the perspective of someone who had not grown up in the area. My ambition was to bring the Seco story to date.

Relating and comparing several centuries of history with recent events which may someday also qualify as history was a new challenge. Several versions of the same event seen through different eyes can exist. Compounding this difficulty is that to some a particular happening may not seem like history or memorable, or maybe something else is history or perhaps should be forgotten. Sometimes a story is embarrassing and is best left untold.

So we listen well and carefully edit the result. While ancient history may not objectively change, new interpretations are frequently proposed. Current events evolve. A description that was true when it was first written oftentimes must be amended. Businesses add and subtract regardless of their longevity. Families change. Restorations are completed. New buildings are constructed, trees grow and fences come down.

I would not have considered this task without the support of Father Vincent Chávez, Larry Torres and his family, Lucío Durán and his family, Palemón Martínez, Abe García, Pablo Quintana, *(Mr. Lucky)*, Arnold and Marco Quintana, and Nancy Carrasco. All of these new friends have suggested fresh trails, have corrected my errors and have oriented me to a *Seco* point of view and time.

Gracias por ayudarme

iv

MAIN STREET ARROYO SECO, 1958
New Mexico State Records and Archives
Photographer Unknown

LA SANTÍSIMA TRINIDAD CHURCH, 1954
Photographer Unknown

LA SANTÍSIMA TRINIDAD CHURCH, 1954
Photographer Unknown

I

A 16TH CENTURY DRY GULLY BECOMES A 20TH CENTURY VILLAGE

Arroyo Seco is a small farming and ranching village in the Taos Valley of northern New Mexico. Best described -- it is a wonderful anachronism -- it is out of time, even for Taos time.[2] Protected by the Sangre de Cristo Range on its eastern flank and the Río Grande Gorge on the west and south, Arroyo Seco has managed to survive-isolated and alone, substantially independent, with little concern for the outside clock. Arroyo Seco is more than the literal translation of its name, which is *dry gully*.

Anchoring the historic community is the original adobe Catholic Church, La Santísima Trinidad (Holy Trinity) completed in 1834. It now sports a new red metal roof, a refurbished bell tower, complete with bell, and restuccoed walls. Its last funeral mass was conducted in 1961 and then, until 1996, the Old Church became the part-time home for several generations of pigeons living above the viga-supported ceiling. The old Spanish bell in the belfry had been sold to pay for the construction of a pitched roof at the turn of the 20th century. The church is surrounded by a plaza and an array of historic buildings. The plaza, built in the early 19th century is itself in restoration. After the Old Church was abandoned as a place of worship, it was relegated to historic church inventory. It housed basketball games, weaving classes, bazaars, dances, and music concerts.

In the late 1980's members of the Holy Trinity parish lobbied the priest and Archdiocese of Santa Fe for permission to restore the structure. Following several years of architectural testing, checking the foundation for movement and seeking various official approvals, volunteers began to clear the area, mold and apply fresh adobe bricks and replaster the interior. Gardens emerged among the cemetery headstones located in front of the large wooden doors of the Church.

Labor and materials were financed by private donations of parishioners, friends, public grants, and community gifts or donated in kind. In less than two years, the disintegrating portions of the walls and foundation were replaced, the interior replastered and painted, wood work cleaned, and new lighting installed. Hand blown glass windows were inserted into vacant frames created by vandalism. Over $125,000 was raised to support the restoration effort in grants and gifts.

Native grass which had invaded the graves located about the perimeter of the church was removed. Fresh flower gardens were planted. The New Mexico Corrections Industries crafted chairs for church pews. Renderings of the original Stations of the Cross decorated the church sidewalks. The Sacristy was furnished to correspond to the early 19th century period including its own fireplace.

The backdrop for the simple church altar is a historic altar screen (reredos) which is a group setting of retablos. It was originally conceived and painted during the construction of the church prior to 1834. During the late 1860's the famous Mexican born santero, José de Gracia Gonzales, repainted and restored these beautiful religious representations of various Saints and the Trinity in oil paints.

The wooden screen is divided into nine separate paintings. At the top of the screen are two three-sided triangles, which are divided into three parts and painted with the colors of the Mexican Flag. Whether the colors represent the fact that de Gracia Gonzales was from Mexico or had some other meaning is unknown. The painter is said to have migrated to the Peñasco region from Mexico. He completed an altar screen in Las Trampas, New Mexico, before transferring his work to Arroyo Seco. Later in life he and his family moved to Trinidad, Colorado.

The Arroyo Seco altar screen has been restored due, in part, to the financial contributions the M. A. Healy Family Foundation and members of the artist's family who continue to reside in the Arroyo Seco area. Restoration of the artwork, which is uniquely New Mexican, has been completed by parish volunteers

HISTORIC ALTAR SCREEN

under the direction of the Museum of New Mexico. The recent acquisition of a dramatically carved Christ on the Cross produced by the famous 19th century Santero, José Rafaél Aragón, was installed on the thick adobe walls of the historic Old Church complementing the de Gracia Gonzales altar screen.[3]

On March 31, 1996, (Passion Sunday) the Old Church reopened. It was blessed by Los Hermanos of the

LA SANTÍSIMA TRINIDAD
Photograph by Te Zin

Penitente Brotherhood *(Fraternidad Piadosa de Nuestro Padre Jesús Nazareno)* who led a traditional procession of parishioners from the Old to the New Church. Due to a fire in the New Church in early 1998, the Old Church resumed the task of a fully functioning place of worship

and celebration of religious activities while the New Church was repaired. After extensive repair, the New Church reopened during the last week in May 1998, and celebratory services were transferred again.

The church restoration committee and Father Chávez coordinated their efforts with numerous public and private foundations and organized weekly Saturday workdays over a two year period. A Restoration Celebration took place with Archbishop Michael Sheehan of Santa Fe, former pastors, sisters and approximately 1,000 persons in attendance on June 7, 1998. The windy open air Mass in the gardens of the Old Church was followed by a traditional community meal.

Outside the newly restored plaza is the unofficial city hall, Abe's Cantina y Cocina. Breakfast burritos, tamales, tacos and chile are prepared by Lina and Olympia. Their father, Abe Garcia, bought his tavern license in 1945 from his uncle after Abe returned from the Second World War. Abe had a dance hall next door,

but tore it down because it was too much trouble. His original building burned in 1975 and friends helped him to rebuild. The bar was carved by hand. Transactions are still conducted in local Spanish dialect and *cinco pesos* (U.S. dollars) can buy a six-pack of beer.

At Casa Fresen a bakery and coffeehouse... neighbors meet over latté, blueberry muffins and the New York Times. A local coyote-dog (belonging to Frank and Barbara Waters) used to sneak under the outdoor tables to intercept wayward croissants. The dog was too friendly and he disappeared. Village business is frequently accomplished under the friendly trees in front of the bakery.  It is said to have been named for the former home of the German Actress, Ali Ghito, who came to Seco following the Second World War. She was a friend of Charlie Chaplin and Hitler. Regardless, the village buried her in a local cemetery.

Taos Cow a creamery operated by young adventurers who were drawn by the ski mountain, elected to stay and produce ice cream. Their product is shipped nationally from their plant located behind the bakery near Ward Art Gallery. A garish version of the Virgen de Guadalupe was found painted on the stucco wall in a local shop - a reminder of the 60's. Villagers affectionately refer to her as *La Nuestra Señora de Choriz* or Our Lady of Baloney. A meat counter used to be located below the painting in earlier days.

The Abominable Snowmansion is home to itinerant travelers in summer -- at cheap rates -- and to skiers in winter -- not so cheap. Behind the building are tepees which can be rented. Annabel's Strictly By Accident moved to Arroyo Seco from its previous location in Ranchos De Taos. Southwestern miscellany brought to town on Annabel's truck and trailer is situated among calculated chaos.

Another storefront goes up for sale. An ancient-forest apricot tree was removed from the parking lot adjoining Casa Fresen to build a new mall where several new shops are located. Not everyone was happy. Something new is change. There is unrelenting turnover in Arroyo Seco commerce and it's not easy to make a living. The longest running new village enterpris-

es are usually a banker's heartbeat away from closing. Survival is still day to day. After 5 years Te Zin's Art Lab closed in October 1998. His photographs of the Old Church

are unforgettable. By November, the building's walls were once again employed to hang art works, this time housing Cooper-Rokoff Contemporary Art.

Several other long time running businesses closed their doors during 1998. The newly established gambling operations at the Taos Pueblo may have unexpectedly impacted the Seco economy. Easily the oldest continuously operating restaurant that unhappily ceased operation was Casa Cordova which had offered fine Continental dining in a 19th century hacienda since 1965. Johnny and Elaine Montaño who owned and operated the *Casa* are still an

important part of the Seco family. The structure has been sold and it will reopen newly refurbished and under new ownership. A much newer food establishment, Deep Fork Smoke House & Grill which was located on the main road lasted almost two years.

The restaurant moved twice and replaced another earlier food establishment that had closed after a short time.

Around the corner and past the old ski lodge that also used to be a country store and once a café is the new Holy Trinity Catholic Church. Its parish

NEW HOLY TRINITY (NEW) CHURCH

HOLY TRINITY PARISH HALL

hall and the rectory which serves as the office and home of Father Vincent P. Chávez are situated immediately south of the Church.

The parish provides for the spiritual and social needs of Arroyo Seco and the nearby communities of Arroyo Hondo, Valdez, Las Colonias and San Cristóbal. It received parish status in 1946. Previously the church was a mission of Our Lady of Guadalupe parish in Taos.

Nearby is the new post office which is two right-angle highway bends away and northeast of the Acequia de la Plaza. It was once a pile of wood stacked for months by the side of the road. The words U.S. Post Office were painted on the edges of the pile that was destined to become the government building. Slowly the new station emerged and now there seem to be plenty of

THE NEW POST OFFICE AS IT LOOKS IN 1998

the mailboxes to serve the growing population. The pictures on the walls haven't changed, however.

THE OLD POST OFFICE AS IT LOOKS IN 1998

La Vieja Loca does business across the road from Abe's Cantina y Cocina in the last old post office (which was one of many). It has no running water or indoor facilities. Only a Vieja Loca could love it and live there. La Vieja Loca used to sit knitting by the side of the narrow road in front of another ramshackle adobe hut further west with an entourage of animals and apprentice knitters. She moved to new quarters in the old post office 100 yards east and built a deck with the help of many friends. Her inventory of art is produced by local artists, weavers from Central America and from parts of what used to be the Ottoman Empire. Original weaving supplements her candy counter income where a nickel will always trade for something. The old location became the home of a vintage clothing shop, first, Olé and today, Otro Mundo situated across the road from Annabel's.

Arroyo Seco gained its own post office in 1895. The life of a postal official here went beyond handling mail and served many roles from distribution of shoes to chickens. The post office has functioned on both sides of the road and in many of the buildings still standing in Seco.[4]

Arroyo Seco is located

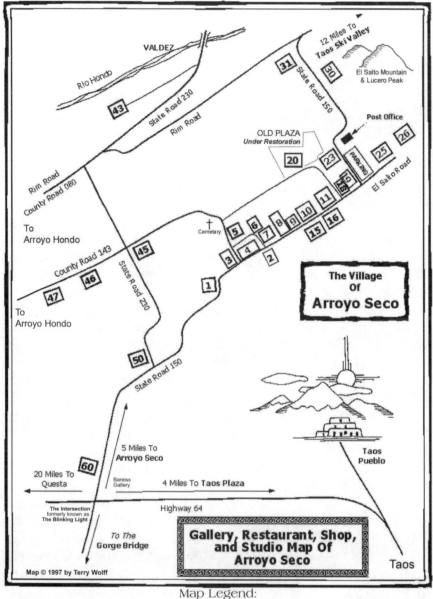

Map Legend:

1) former Casa Cordova Restaurant
2) Private home
3) Abominable Snowmansion
4) former Deep Fork Smokehouse & Grill
5) A.C. Ward Gallery & Studio
6) Taos Cow Ice Cream Co.
7) Casa Fresen Bakery, Cafe & Deli
8) Burkina
   Claire Works
   Las Comadres Gallery
   Premiere Properties
   Siena
9) Cooper-Rokoff Contemporary Arts
10) Annabel's Strictly by Accident
11) Italian Restaurant
15) Otro Mundo, vintage clothing

16) Abe's Cantina y Cocina
18) La Vieja Loca
19) Old Ski Lodge
20) La Santisima Trinidad Church
23) Holy Trinity Parish Hall
25) Taos Mountain Bed & Breakfast
30) Salsa del Salto Bed & Breakfast
31) Adobe & Stars Bed & Breakfast
43) Artes del Lobo / Gray Wolf Trading Co.
45) Violetta's Grocery Store
46) Alma del Monte Bed & Breakfast
47) Little Tree Bed & Breakfast
50) Cottonwood Inn Bed & Breakfast
60) All About Taos, Tim's Chile Connection,
    Piñon Investments, Taos Kangaroo,
    Quail Ridge, Los Rios River Runners

about eight miles northeast of the Taos city limits. State Highway 230, the road to the Ski Valley and Valdez, divides and becomes Highway 150 which branches easterly toward the mountain range, Arroyo Seco and then the Hondo Canyon. An older and narrower road begins in front of the Abominable Snowmansion in the middle of the village and winds northwesterly passing the cemetery, apple trees and farms. An imaginary line drawn through the decorated graves of the *camposanto* marks an informal boundary with the community of Des Montes. A sign is posted at the cemetery reminding visitors that the final resting-place for generations is a holy place. Sketching and photography are not permitted.

The Hondo-Seco Road passes the new Arroyos del Norte Elementary School and drops several hundred feet to Arroyo Hondo. It twists by Nuestra Señora de Dolores Catholic Church (c. 1830) which itself has been recently restored and is part of the Holy Trinity Parish. From there, the road follows the Hondo River and ends at Herb's Lounge at State Highway 522 several miles west. Ten miles north of Herb's is Questa and another 20 miles north is Costilla and the Colorado-New Mexico border. The dividing line between these two states was established at the 37th

NUESTRA SEÑORA DE DOLORES (circa 1830)

parallel in 1861 when part of the original New Mexican territory was annexed to the newly created Colorado Territory.

Historic homes dating to the 19th century are located on the north side of El Salto Road that branches toward the mountain at the currently vacant elementary school.

Livestock and vegetable gardens flank the Taos Mountain Bed & Breakfast which is easily identified by the Tepee on the front lawn. Guests of the Torrez family share an unparalleled view of the Peak and waterfall. In the spring the Arroyo Seco Creek overflows, spreading water over the fields and roads. The south side of El Salto Road is the Taos Pueblo land referred to as the Tenorio Tract. It was transferred to the Pueblo in 1934 following a court decision involving title to the

NUESTRA SEÑORA DE DOLORES
(circa 1830)

property that had been purchased by the Pueblo for 5500 pesos.

The federal decision in the Tenorio Tract lawsuit validated claims advanced by the Taos Pueblo to that section of land which the Pueblo had purchased from Spanish sellers over 100 years earlier. Arroyo Seco farmers were the losers. A condemnation action resulted from the case which provided for a small payment to Seco farmers who had constructed buildings and some homes in the area over a number of years. The occupation of the Tenorio Tract following the Pueblo purchase is said to have occurred at the encouragement of a local tax assessor.[5]

NUESTRA SEÑORA DE DOLORES
ENTRANCEWAY

The Tenorio lawsuit and its aftermath resulted in continuing land and water issues facing these two neighboring villages. The property was fenced by the Pueblo which cut off historic trade between the two communities. The fence is little deterrent; however, to buffalo that sometimes break

11

through the fence to visit the village, shop owners and their customers.

The end of El Salto Road is private property which is plainly announced on a sign posted by a green house. Another sign affixed to the school fence proclaims that Bikers are strictly forbidden on the waterfall trail. For a small charge, hikers can climb to the waterfall. Once in awhile, the sound of a rifle reminds trespassers that the property is private. It is owned by a group of original families who invested in the land and who have allowed it to remain open space for their use.

Nearby, the magical El Salto de las Aguas and Lucero Peak with numerous waterfalls visible in the spring from the village capture the winter and spring snowfall so that the Arroyo Seco Creek and water from the conjoining Río Lucero Ditch can fill the acequias (ditches). Frozen skeletons of ice frame the rocky outcroppings of El Salto in the winter. Cottonwoods and willows that line the creek and the acequias become golden in the fall and define the banks. After several hard frosts, the creek flows below the ice which is covered with broken limbs, willow bark and accumulations of grass. During a thaw, mud emerges and becomes the common theme of country living. *Mud* and *Seco* mean the same in spring.

El Salto and Lucero Peaks are situated east of town. The winter sun sets behind the Perdernal at the western village of Abiquiú where Georgia O'Keefe lived and painted. It

casts an indirect light some people call Greek light on El Salto and Lucero Peak for a few seconds. In March the air is clear of dust and views west across the mesa for 100 miles or more are usual. During the summer the same light illuminates the clouds behind the mountain and its family range, creating a reddish pink foam or Sangre de Cristo. The range was named after the holy blood of Christ believed to shroud the mountains in the valley.

The Pueblo land on the south, even though partially irrigated, is, for the most part, open, natural, and dry. Few buildings can be seen. Cattle, buffalo and ponies range through the sage, yucca, chamisa and cactus. There used to be more rabbits everywhere. Now the smart rabbits stay away. Once in a while young men from the Taos Pueblo dam up the Lucero Ditch to catch fish which interrupted water flow to the village ditches. It is then that the Arroyo Seco Acequia Commission calls for emergency meetings with the Pueblo to reopen the ditch. The headwater of Río Lucero and its main diversion is located on the Pueblo land. Suggestions to share the control of the headgates which are on the Pueblo land have not been implemented.

From the late 17th century, Arroyo Seco was home to the Pueblo and Spanish cultures. Then a few Americans, arrived during the 19th century from the north. Now a fourth culture –skiers – try not to stop in Seco in their rush for the valley, deep powder and brilliant sunny skies. The impact of the skiing culture has been considerable and apparent.

There is evidence of a fifth culture (a transitional culture) that is aging rapidly. The archaeological remains appear at unexpected times. Periodically it is in the air. Nuevo fifth culture is not fifth culture. These are wannabees who follow the roads in faux corn rolls. The originals were called hippies. They came in the late 1960's and were not greeted with open arms. At times they were forcefully excluded - sometimes at Abe's. A few stayed on. Some wrote books. Some even made movies and toured the country on motorcycles, advocating various freedoms. Many eventually reverted to farming to produce organic foods. A few succeeded and evolved and became carpenters, contractors and artists of note.

Drawn by the isolation and, at the same time, the need to proclaim an alternative life style, the fifth culture abruptly atrophied following President Nixon's retirement speech. After Johnson and Nixon nobody was left to fight who seemed worthy to fight. Families emerged from the fifth culture. Now there is integration and it is difficult to recognize a third-generation fifth culture descendant except that they appear to vote and dress more conservatively than their forebears.

A proto-sixth culture has emerged. Texans, Californians, Coloradans, and immigrants from Michigan and New York now call Seco their part-time home. They concern themselves in art, literature, music, and history and drive sports utility vehicles. These well-meaning residents seek the diversions of sport, the natural beauty and friendliness of the village, the out-of-doors and a slower lifestyle than the one that waits at home.

Arroyo Seco is old. It lies in the middle of an important watershed. It was one of the first sites settled by the first culture who may have arrived from Chaco Canyon to the north and constructed pit houses in the ground near the rivers. They were probably Anasazi wanderers. Except to purists, the exact source or the form of their name does not matter. These ancients were the First People in the area and they predated the Taos Pueblo which we call, here, the First Culture.[6] The Spanish which was The Second Culture, arrived with Don Juan de Oñate in 1598 and established a stronghold near the San Juan Pueblo on the Río Grande. 1998, is, therefore, the 400th anniversary of the *entrada* of The Second Culture.

The oldest things are mostly buried. You can't really say they are gone because you can feel the old and it's there –somewhere -- just covered by newer things which are old too. In Arroyo Seco sometimes what is old and beautiful to one person is another's discard. It may seem that some of the shops and homes are in need of work. But part of the statement made by Seco is just that -- being in need of work. Nothing new is good. Fix the old. Don't go overboard and it works.

Architecture in Arroyo Seco varies dramatically. Adobe mixes with almost anything. There are tepees, A-frames, ranches, traditional adobe buildings, mobile homes, double-wides, territorial castles or mud walls filled with glass bottles or hay. Peeling stucco exposing the straw and mud brick is warm and friendly. Add some stucco and it's as good as new and just as friendly. Put something on your roof. It doesn't have to be a birdhouse, it can be a wagon if you want.

Distant stars, comets asteroids and the moon rising over Lucero Peak light up the night sky. This fire from beyond has concentrated its candle power on this singular village. The natural forces of the universe have not acci-dentally aligned themselves by quirk in their nightly display over Arroyo Seco. The light keeps the Bad Spirit away.

After the sun has set, the bear follows the acequia eating berries along the way, depositing bear deposits and checking out barrels. The bear is a natural recycler of people stuff which is abun-

ON LEFT IS ONE OF THE ART LAB'S INSTALLA-TIONS, NOT TO BE OUT DONE BY THE LAB'S OUTHOUSE ON THE RIGHT

dant along the acequia and by the roads. Night hawks, coyotes and raccoons love the night and people stuff, too. Daytime is for rainbows and in the spring and summer they start over by the Hondo Canyon and stretch to the village. Oftentimes, double rainbows frame the Peak. Rainbows avoid hard edges. The many colors work together. Seco seems a lot like a rainbow.

The fields around Arroyo Seco define its character. They confine the ubiquitous cattle and flocks of bleating sheep. A bell cow hunkered down in its munching position making bell sounds is often the only sound competing with the "yak, yak, yak" of magpies and jays. Alfalfa, brome and wild grasses are usually plentiful. Several hay cuttings are often made depending on weather. Fall alfalfa, highly rich in protein, produces fields of deeply hued purple flowers. Alfalfa roots descend to the center of the earth. Fields are outlined by fences, sunflowers and cattails. Iris pop up here and there, and asparagus shoots emerge in wet places.

Fields represent generations of history. They are part of a family's heritage and are divided among children, divided and divided again – all with access to the acequia or Río. Some fields are held in trust so that they can be preserved for the future. Farmers feed their cattle during the winter in the fields dropping baled hay in the snow. Coyotes, foxes, dogs and cats claim the fields as their home as well as their dinner table.

Distance is measured by fields. Directions are given by fields. Fields hide cowbirds, which aspire to be the most irascible creatures on earth. They conspire to steal nests during the spring from Red Wing Blackbirds, promiscuously mate and unprovokedly attack scrubjays and humans from their home base in the fields. Arroyo Seco fields are the subject of paintings, writings and songs. Fields persist and endure despite efforts to convert them to industrial or residential uses.

Arroyo Seco loves its fields, and rightly so. These open spaces constitute a green belt and are a constant reminder of its Hispanic farming and ranching heritage. The fields are the home to meadowlarks, water snakes, moles and prairie dogs. And you can ride a pony in a field without fear of colliding with someone from the fourth culture driving a newly-rented Toyota intent on finding the ski valley before the powder is gone.

II

CULTURES COLLIDE IN 17TH AND 18TH CENTURIES

Arroyo Seco is not really dry. It's wet a lot of the time. 1996 was an aberrant exception to this usual condition. During the spring, water usually flows rapidly down the Arroyo Seco Creek and from Río Lucero into the main acequia (ditch) through its four primary lateral branches spilling across the State Highway 150 in Seco and flooding the lower fields in an intricate network of meanders.

The acequias go through and around the village plaza irrigating gardens and fields.  Water is a few feet below the surface of the ground and usually easy to reach with a well. Surface irrigation through the ditch system, however, provides the traditional approach to farming. Water has dictated the destiny of the people in this community for at least 250 years. The arid and desert-like lands which are within a few miles to the west prove that the difference between wet or dry, fertile or barren, rich or poor is a very fine line. It is always at hand and easy to cross. The importance of water is often lost on visitors. Here, Water is Life.

The old Arroyo Seco was periodically, seco (dry). Around the year 1745, the original settlers may have located near an arroyo which is now dry and is located a few fields northeast of the current village. An arroyo is a gulch or ditch created by erosion of the soil caused by the flow of water. When rain periodically came from the mountain and down the waterfall (El Salto de las Aguas) the arroyo ran full. Then it was dry again.

That the dry arroyo even exists suggests that at some time in the past it flowed more continuously and the area was much wetter than it is today. Archeological studies of desert varnish support the theory that the Southwest endured cycles of heavy rainfall and dramatic drought.[7] While scientists now say the always changeable weather is controlled by a phenomenon involving Pacific currents called El Niño, many residents of Arroyo Seco have believed this to be the case for centuries and will say so on any occasion but their point of reference is Jesús, El Niño, and not an ocean current.

Standing in a peaceful and secluded tree lined dirt road reflecting on the simplicity of the morada (the 1870 Penitente meeting house) and the independent spirit of this community, it is difficult to visualize the conflict and hardship which were the historical hallmarks of the village. Few stories report contacts that pre-date Coronado's southern march in 1539 and Espejo's reports of his 1582 expedition. Both missed Arroyo Seco, although isolated incursions into the area were reportedly made by small exploring units associated with those Spanish expeditions.

By then, the nearby Taos Pueblo

TAOS PUEBLO VILLAGE
(approx. 600 years old)
Photo by Pueblo photographer Bruce Gomez

had been occupied for at least 250 years. But even so, the Pueblo culture was not first around Seco. The very first people likely came from the north and built pit houses for their families. Recently unearthed structures of semi-nomadic people, which may date from 800 A.D., located south of Arroyo Seco (where the blinking light used to be located), indicate that early migrations and their resulting collisions occurred at least 1200 years ago in these parts.[8]

The Spanish explorers came from the southeast, also following the water. They collided with several Pueblo cultures after each had followed the Río Del Norte from different directions in different periods during the 1598 march of Juan de Oñate who was accompanied by 130 families in a march into the forbidding North. Oñate brazenly claimed control over a huge territory including what was to become The Kingdom of New Mexico.

Oñate's conquest was accomplished with relatively little bloodshed by modern standards. 1998 is the 400 year anniversary of the incursion. However, not all New Mexicans celebrate the occasion. The Acoma Pueblo, among others, has protested the memory. Oñate brutally punished the Acomas and other

PLAZA AT THE TAOS PUEBLO VILLAGE
Photo by Pueblo photographer Bruce Gomez

Pueblos for their resistance - slight as it may have been – and then was tried and convicted by the Spanish for the atrocities. He was stripped of his titles and ordered never to return to New Mexico. Memories, even those which are 400 years old, do not fade easily.[9]

The history of Arroyo Seco is a story of colliding cultures. The land, the water, the air, the bear, eagle, coyote and trout were first. People, who came later, oftentimes forget that we are the relative newcomers. To be first is important. But, if you cannot be first, then it is almost as important to be before someone else. In an isolated and co-dependent community, standing is important. Being first is especially important in water priority proceedings, which have continued to dominate cultural and political issues in this area.

Besides drama, tragedy and comedy, the collision of cultures evokes change. Change often can be traumatic. Even though the change may be a natural evolution of ideas or ways, the person who can be identified as instigating change frequently became an outcast and an outcast who lived 1200 years ago probably died horribly.

Opposing rapid change are group values, which qualify as tradition or custom. Tradition is important in Arroyo Seco. Traditional ways of living have bound generations of families together despite influences from the outside, which sometimes are considered destructive. People acting in identifiable ways over years are said to have customs and a culture. The nearby Taos Pueblo also has been considered to be actively traditionalist to the point of opposing electricity and piped water into their homes on the Pueblo after it became available.[10]

For 82 years following Oñate's 1598 introduction to the Tiwa-speaking Taos Pueblo inhabitants, the two cultures cohabited near Arroyo Seco. Attempts by the Spanish military leaders to enforce traditions and customs of the Iberian culture and the efforts of Franciscan Friars bent on religious conversion led to more conflict. Sometime before 1680, a Spanish soldier, Sergeant Major Diego Lucero de Godoy, received a royal Merced or land grant from the Spanish king for an area comprising approximately 60,000 acres, which included Arroyo Seco. A local river and mountain appear to bear his name –Lucero Peak – although the origin of the peak's name may be related to its location of the position of the planet Venus as it rises in the east. The home of Lucero de Godoy was reported to have been located near the bank of a river a few miles south of Arroyo Seco-probably Río Lucero. Lucero never returned to the area following the 1680 revolt of the Pueblos.[11]

Settlers associated with Lucero may have been responsible for building a first primitive torreón (tower) for defense, which was studied by Jeffrey L. Boyer in 1990. The tower location is on a commanding high plateau very close to the old Arroyo Seco location. The scientific work of

Mr. Boyer was related to water – the attempt to document and date when water was first used by the Seco farmers for irrigation.

Following several decades of imposition of Spanish laws, Spanish religion, Spanish language, the inculcation of slavery and collection of taxes, the Pueblos along the Río Grande, including the Taos Pueblo secretly combined for battle. Organized under local leaders and a war chief called Popé, who often resided at the Taos Pueblo, the Pueblos up and down the Rio Grande and its tributaries revolted on August 10, 1680. Sergeant Major Lucero de Godoy was in El Paso del Norte, which is now part of Texas, on military business and avoided death.

Most Spanish men and Franciscan clergy were either killed or driven south to El Paso along with the surviving and embarrassed Spanish Governor Otermín whose capitol was in Santa Fe. Each side engaged in some form of genocide during the fight. The victorious Pueblo Indians outlawed Spanish customs and the cultures violently separated. Surviving Spanish women captured during the conflagration were retained as servant consorts to the conquering Pueblos.[12]

Popé and his supporters occupied Santa Fe, destroyed Spanish documents which were believed to be symbols of power and attempted to centralize an indigenous government. The 1680 destruction of records had an important later impact on the proof of title to land since possession of actual legal documents was a customary method of showing ownership of the land.

Several abortive attempts by the Spanish to re-conquer and re-populate the lost territory failed. Ultimately, the breakdown of the central political and military organization among the Pueblos due, in part, to jealousy and envy, followed after only 12 years of indigenous self-government. Employing both military and diplomatic tactics, Governor Don Diego De Vargas Zapate Luján Ponce de León y Contreras (De Vargas), who was described by Robert Silverberg as cultured, devout, self-disciplined, elegant and fearing nothing but God, reoccupied the disputed New Mexican Kingdom of New Spain between 1692 and 1696.[13]

The 1692 re-conquest by De Vargas sometimes called

the Last Conquistador was described as peaceful. De Vargas' first act in approaching Santa Fe was to cut off the Indians' supply of water from the river.[14] Taos Pueblo was surrounded by De Vargas forces but the Spanish found it empty. Eventually, the distrusting Taos warriors and their families were convinced to return from their mountain hideout to the Pueblo. Following pacification Franciscan Friars once again took up residence in many of the Pueblos including Taos.

In 1696 many of the Franciscan missionaries again withdrew to Santa Fe fearing a renewed Pueblo revolt. Unable to reach the safety of the capitol, Fray Antonio Carbonel of the Taos Pueblo was killed at the Pueblo of San Cristóbal on June 4, 1696. Other Franciscans were also martyred. Fray Francisco de Vargas, the newly appointed custodian of the Franciscan New Mexican custody, (a jurisdictional area established by the religious hierarchy) led a military force to Taos. He convinced the Pueblo, once again, to peacefully return from their mountain to the Pueblo.[15]

Following the forced submission of the Picurís Pueblo, the revolt collapsed and was soon concluded in the Spaniards' favor. In 1697 there were apparently only 1500 Spanish-speaking persons in the New Mexican colony.[16] These few controlled a huge area of land and many persons living on the land. By 1790 the Spanish population had increased to 15,000. Pueblo elders probably had no notion that the Spanish king of Arroyo Seco in 1716 was Charles II, the last Spanish Austrian Hapsburg and the retarded son of Phillip the IV. Charles was called the bewitched King of Spain. Had they known the true state of Spanish politics, the revolutionary events of 1680 and 1696 could well have been repeated with more success.

As a result of De Vargas reconquest, the Cultures recollided. The Arroyo Seco land grant previously ceded to Lucero de Godoy was occupied by Don Antonio Martínez who received a 1716 re-grant of the same lands from the Spanish governor. The Martínez land grant was bounded on the west by the Río Grande, on the south by the Río Lucero, on the east by the mountains, and on the north by the Río Hondo.

Antonio Martínez' heirs settled near the Arroyo Seco

Creek and built ditches to irrigate the fields. The precise date that this construction took place has remained in dispute for almost two centuries. Establishing an earlier date than 1815 for the Arroyo Seco diversion of water still is a primary objective in the water debate. Cristóbal Martínez and José Gregorio Martínez planted crops in the Arroyo Seco area between 1804 and 1807. Planting would have required existing irrigation indicating an earlier priority date for water rights.[17]

The farmers in Seco concerned themselves with fending off raids by raiding tribes of Nomadic Indians using the torreón built on the high plateau on the east side of the village near El Salto. The tower had undergone periodic reconstruction according to archeological surveys conducted by Jeffrey Boyer.[18] If Boyer is correct in dating the tower to approximately 1745 then the village can claim an organized history of over 250 years.

Arroyo Seco was largely ignored from the beginning of the 19th century for almost 130 years. Nine Spanish monarchies began and ended. These kings were partly or wholly of French and Austrian blood. Separated from mainstream commerce, the farmers of Arroyo Seco worked the land as Spanish custom decreed and completed the complicated series of ditches that irrigate the land. These ditches still provide for irrigation water distribution as they did 250 years ago.

Spain's own revolution of 1820, which was intended to limit the power of its conservative clergy and nobility, ironically resulted in a conservative rebellion in Mexico led by local clergy. In 1821 the Spanish Viceroy was forced to accede to Mexican demands for independence. Spain had previously sealed the eastern borders between the United States and New Mexico out of fear of American expansionism. Mexican independence revised that closed-door policy and the new trade along the Santa Fe and Taos trails presaged a third collision of cultures.

Traders and trappers of northern European blood were perceived to rudely exploit Spanish women in the Taos Valley. Taos cantina brawls frequently occurred between White Indians, (trappers adhering to no set of social rules) who were inflamed by locally distilled Taos Lightning and disgusted Spanish farmers. Crude, irreligious and nomadic, the new Anglo visitors antagonized Hispanic and Pueblo elders.

Adding to the mix was the claim of newly independent Texas to the portion of New Mexico lying east of the Rio Grande. Periodically, Texans invaded New Mexico committing various forms of depredation. Another violent collision of the cultures followed the 1846 declaration of war on Mexico by the expansionist United States government of James K. Polk. In the name of Manifest Destiny, General Stephen Kearney invaded and occupied New Mexico, which was a department of the Republic of Mexico while other military adventures were pursued in California and in

THE MURDER OF NEW MEXICO GOVERNER
CHARLES BENT IN 1847
Painting by Larry Torres

Mexico. A year before the war ended, on January 19, 1847, a combined force of Hispanic and Pueblo warriors attacked and killed Charles Bent, the provisionally appointed military Governor of the occupied New Mexico at his Bent Street home in Don Fernando de Taos.[19] Turley's Mill in the Arroyo Hondo Valley a few miles northwest of Seco and an important distiller of Taos Lightning was sacked. Its owner Simeon Turley and his friends were also killed.[20]

SAN JERÓNIMO CHURCH AT THE TAOS PUEBLO
(DISTROYED BY AMERICAN TROOPS ON FEB 4, 1847)
Photo by Pueblo photographer Bruce Gomez

Captain Burgwin, who died during the resulting battle between the U.S. Dragoons and the Taos guerrillas, surrounded the historic San Jerónimo

SAN JERÓNIMO CHURCH AT THE
TAOS PUEBLO, 1930'S
Source unknown

Church in the Taos Pueblo on February 4, 1847, a few miles south of Seco. It is reported that 282 Mexican rebels were killed. By comparison, 15 American troops lost their lives. On February 7, 1847, the leader of the insurgents was executed after a military trial. Fourteen other rebels were similarly dispatched.[21] Because the church was being used as a fort for the dissidents, it was pounded into rubble by American artillery rounds and so it remains today surrounded by gravesites which are both old and new.

Numerous of the combatant ringleaders who were taken prisoners as a result of the conflict were tried by prosecutors using the English language although the defendants only spoke Spanish.[22] They were then hung as traitors. The charge

SAN JERÓNIMO CHURCH AT THE TAOS PUEBLO, 1990'S
Photo by Pueblo photographer Bruce Gomez

of treason was made even though the Treaty of Guadalupe Hidalgo which ceded New Mexico, Arizona, and parts of Colorado and Wyoming to the United States for $15 million was not signed until nine months later on February 2, 1848. New Mexico remained in political disequilibrium or limbo for three years until it was granted Territorial status in 1851 by Congress.

WINTER AT THE TAOS PUEBLO VILLAGE
Photo by Pueblo photographer Bruce Gomez

III

LAND CONTROVERSIES DOMINATE 19TH CENTURY

Bloody civil war in Spain during the first decade of the 19th century led to the reign of the despotic Spanish monarch, Ferdinand VII and, ultimately, independence in Mexico. Protesting the Spanish chaos, Francisco Goya, the king's liberal court painter, fearfully hid his masterpiece works of art depicting the Civil War. Paranoia swept the European nation and its possessions across the ocean.

The Mexican War of Independence was initiated by Father Miguel Hidalgo y Costilla who was assisted by Ignacio de Allende in Dolores de Hidalgo, New Spain, on September 15, 1810. Their execution in 1811 by the King and the subsequent gruesome display of their heads in cages on the four corners of a government building in Guanajuato, New Spain, emboldened revolutionary activities by Padre José María Morelos - also later executed. General Augustín de Iturbide, a royalist who had opposed the revolutionaries, switched sides. Independence was proclaimed in 1821 with Iturbide humbly assuming the title of Emperor.

During the same period, abject isolation in Spanish New Mexico fostered the artistic explosion of Laguna Santero and his followers whose religious paintings of the saints (retablos) have only recently been recognized as a distinct art form. Conflicts involving land in the Spanish Province of New Mexico[23] were frequent and mimed Spain's territorial tribulations. In and around Arroyo Seco a dispute among family members of Antonio Martín resulted in local civil unrest. Lengthy and protracted litigation, a different kind of warfare, engaged the two sides of the Martín heirs for decades.

In 1745 Governor Joaquín Cordallo y Rabal granted Antonio Martín (not to be confused with Antonio Martínez) a

tract of land comprising the same ground that Antonio Martínez had been ceded in 1716 (the Lucero de Godoy tract). Historic records do not disclose why the tract was re-granted again since Martínez heirs still apparently resided in Arroyo Seco. Adding to the puzzle and confusion another grant in 1742 to Pedro de Santillánes comprising some of the same lands was made by the Governor. Copies of these grants are available on microfilm in the Spanish Archives of New Mexico in Santa Fe. Either the Governor did not realize his mistake or he intentionally made grants of overlapping

BULTO BY THE "LAGUNA SANTERO" HANGING
IN THE ARROYO SECO CHURCH

grants believing that it would be worked out some day.

Arroyo Seco pioneers sought to base their claim to land title upon the October 7, 1745 grant by Governor Rabal to Martín.[24] This grant was made after the Martínez Grant became law. Nonetheless the Martín grant was offered as evidence in establishing title in later adverse possession proceedings. Legal title can be established by claiming that the claimant has adversely occupied the land in question for a designated period of time.

Antonio Martín's heirs died without a will and the ensuing fight between his heirs, the Sanches family and his Martín heirs was acrimonious and expensive. The Sanches heirs constructed ditches, buildings and the Arroyo Seco Plaza between 1806 and 1815 to buttress their land claim. Such are the beginnings of adverse possession. Apparently begun in 1816, the ensuing lawsuit was finalized in 1826 by the El Prado alcalde, a combination mayor and judge, who met with the legal combatants at the Arroyo Seco sitio (site).

It was determined that Antonio Martín, who received the 1745 land grant that overlay the Antonio Martínez Grant had fathered a child with his niece, Isabel Pacheco. His resulting natural son, Diego Rafaél, became father to Manuel and Matías Martín who made claim to the Martín estate. After Antonio died, (but after he had also produced another child by an extramarital relationship with Isabel's sister) Isabel married Francísco Sanches and gave birth to four children who were litigants with the Martín clan. Antonio had given Isabel and her sister the lands in question prior to his death. Isabel and her sister unfortunately died without creating a will to direct ownership of their assets after death. Isabel's sister's illegitimate child did not survive her mother.

The parties agreed to divide the 1745 grant, with the Sanches family taking the property lying north of Arroyo Seco Creek and the Martín family taking the property on the south side to forever settle the matter, and thereby, naturally, creating a dispute that endures. Almost immediately, the Martín family sold its interest to the Taos Pueblo for 5500 pesos through its agent Miguel Tenorio. The land became known as the Tenorio Tract. That transaction impacted water and land difficulties that continue until today and it was responsible for the court ordered transfer of Arroyo Seco farmlands to the Pueblo in 1934.

The 1826 settlement agreement also subdivided the Sanches portion of the tract among family members. The Alcade reported, "... *José Antonio Sanches was allowed 450 varas, it being understood that of these one hundred are in the upper part in front of the plaza, on account of a trade which José Antonio Sanches had made with his uncle, Varlano Sanches*".[25] The parcels were measured along Arroyo Seco Creek by varas or 33-inch long sticks, which were closely equivalent to a man's pace. The fact that these lands had been earlier ceded to Antonio Martínez in another land grant document seems to have not been of issue in this litigation. By then, possession was more important than a piece of paper.

Various workers who had helped the Sanches family construct the ditches and buildings received individual plots of land. The parcels ran north and south between the Arroyo Seco Creek and the Cuchilla (ridge) of the Hondo Valley. The plaza, which had been built before the settlement by the Sanches family, served primarily as a defensive function. New Mexican communities had been ordered by the military leaders to consolidate scattered settlements into more compact units in 1778. The Bishop of Durango responsible for the New Mexican province granted a license to build a mission church in Arroyo Seco in 1826 which was completed in 1834.

The plaza referred to in the alcalde's decision lies outside the Old Church. It is irrigated and delineated by La Acequia de la Plaza on the north side. Buildings completely surrounded the plaza as prescribed security. The 1834 church became the central focus of the plaza. Further restoration of the plaza, remains as part of the overall Church project. The drawing and map of the Plaza on pages 32 and 33 were prepared by Larry Torres. The map documents several generations of ownership of plaza buildings and homes.

Because water is distributed in New Mexico according to the doctrine of priority of use, village claimants to the ditch water flowing from Río Lucero through the main ditch (Acequia Madre), which intersects Arroyo Seco Creek, attempted to show various early dates of first use in court proceedings. The claim that the Arroyo Seco lands had been irrigated since 1747 from Río Lucero and its major lateral ditches, Temporales, Torreón, Alamitos and Espinazo has not yet been accepted.

A local court decree in 1942 established the appropriation date for Arroyo Seco farmers and ranchers as 1815. The water dispute history and case law are reported in a study by John O. Baxter. The water priority debate continues. Adjudication proceedings started in 1969 involving rights on the Río Grande, Río Pueblo and Río Lucero, remains to be decided.[27]

A water dispute between the Antonio Martín heirs and the Taos Pueblo was decided in 1823 by an alcalde who allocated one surco of water to be taken by Arroyo Seco, but only during times of abundant water. One *surco* is approximately the volume of water that can pass through the hub of a Mexican wagon wheel of usual size. Another confrontation resulted when the Pueblo placed a wagon wheel into the main ditch from the Río Lucero to restrict water usage down ditch to one surco. That meant that the water flow was restricted to the volume that could pass through one hub. Arroyo Seco farmers planned a physical battle. It was fortunately averted by the divine intervention of a flood which rendered the dispute moot.[28]

Padre Antonio José Martínez gave testimony in another water lawsuit between Arroyo Seco and the Pueblo in 1864. The resulting decision allotted Arroyo Seco three surcos of water when the river flow exceeded 15 surcos in capacity.[29] This influential Catholic pastor published the first newspaper (El Crepúsculo), started a school in Taos, served in the Territorial Legislature as its Council President, founded an important Taos family and managed to be excommunicated from the church due to disagreements with the French Archbishop, Jean Baptiste Lamy.

In 1893 Seco villagers filed another water rights case. Judge Seed awarded 30% of the Lucero flow of water to Arroyo Seco and 35% each to the Pueblo and El Prado. Any surplus was to go to Arroyo Seco Abajo which is called Las Colonias now.[30] In 1945 in the New Mexico state case of Martínez v. Martínez, the Supreme Court reviewed the history of Arroyo Seco's award of 30% of the flow of Río Lucero.[31] Apparently, a committee representing Arroyo Seco Arriba (upper Arroyo Seco) contended that the Pueblo used almost 47% of the water reducing the flow to Arroyo Seco to 18% of the available water.

The Pueblo had argued that the State had no power to regulate the Pueblo's water use. The Supreme Court of New Mexico said that the Tenorio Tract which had been purchased with 5500 pesos was within the jurisdiction of the State and it decided that the court did have the power to award 30% of the water flow to Arroyo Seco. An irony of the water wars is that the Pueblo's legal argument was based upon a Spanish land grant which it bought from the Martín clan rather than by natural, or aboriginal right. Thus, the Pueblo invoked rights created by land grant, which rights the

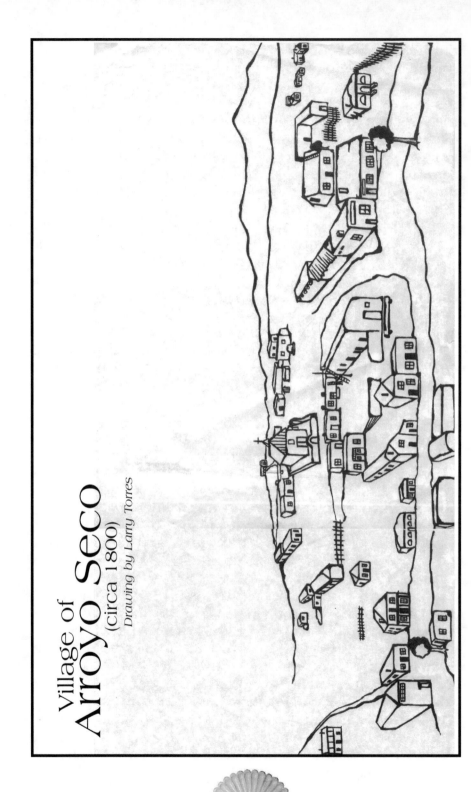

Village of
Arroyo Seco
(circa 1800)
Drawing by Larry Torres

Mapa Histórico de Arroyo Seco, Nuevo México

(Not to scale)

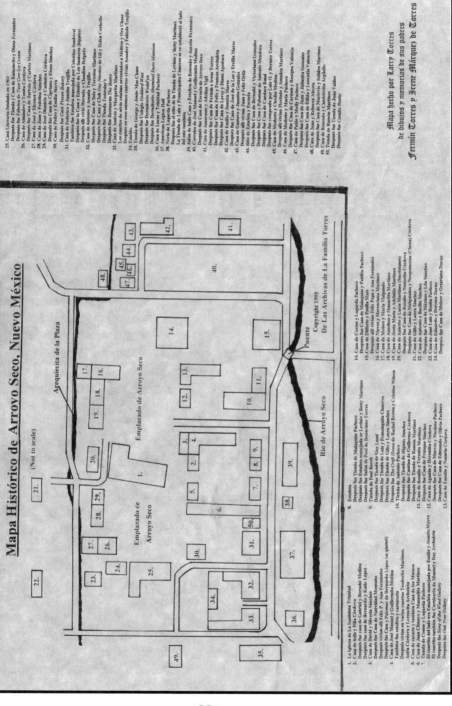

Acequieria de la Plaza

Emplazado de Arroyo Seco

Emplazado de Arroyo Seco

Puente

Río de Arroyo Seco

Copyright 1995
De Las Archivas de La Familia Torres

1. La Iglesia de La Santísima Trinidad
2. Casa de Sulú y Ella Córdova
3. Después fue casa de Gabriel y Bernabé Medina
   Después fue casa de Bernardo y Katie López
4. Casa de David y Silveria Montaño
5. Después vivían allí Félix P. y Ana Fernández
   Después fue Casa y Palomar de Bernardo López (se quemó)
6. Casa de José Manuel y Guillermina Medina
   Después vivían en varios cuartos Teodorita Martínez,
   Anita Córdova y Leveneita Archuleta
7. Casa de encinito y también Casa de las Marras
   Casa de Juan Clímaco y Mónica Martínez
   Tienda de Cosme y Laguerda Pacheco
   El cuartito del lado era Estafeta manejada por Emilio y Juanita Marra
   El cuartito también fue Carnicería de Manuel y Ray Archuleta
   Después fue Bric-a-Brac of the Oak Tree Gallery
   Después fue Oak Tree Gallery
8. Estafeta
   Después fue Tienda de Malaquías Pacheco
   Después fue Estafeta manejada por Levbio y Betty Martínez
   Después fue Salón de Peol de Donaciano Torres
9. Tienda de Paul Bareis
   Después fue Tienda de Luis y Franchiquita Cisneros
   Después fue Tienda de Celso y Laura Sánchez
   Después fue The Craft House de Rachel Brown y Cristina Wilson
10. Tienda de Antonio Pacheco
    Después fue tienda de Elpidio Sánchez
    Después fue Cantina de Guillermo Córdova
    Después fue Tienda de Ramón Martínez
11. Casa de Rosalía y Ferminita Martínez
    Después fue Casa de Amos Nusio
12. Casa de Agustín y Herminita Córdova
    Después fue Casa de Marcos y Nicolasa Pacheco
    Después fue Casa de Edmundo y Silvia Pacheco
13. Casa de Yámilo y Nazaria Córdova

14. Casa de Cosme y Laguerda Pacheco
15. Después fue Casa de Malaquías y Fabila Pacheco
    Casa de Dilferio y Emilia Mars
    Después allí vivían Félix Papa y Ana Fernández
16. Casa de Nieves y Merveciana Martínez
17. Después fue Tienda de Cilio y María Vialpando
18. Casa de Acineno y Manuelita Martínez
19. Casa de Jesús María y Adelaida Martínez
20. Casa de Aniceto y Lucia Martínez (Sacristanes)
    Después fue Casa de Rosalía y Nestorcita Córdova
    Después fue Casa de Melquiades y Neoponicena (Chona) Córdova
21. Casa de Cilio y Laura Sánchez
22. Casa de Antonio y Bacilia Sánchez
    Después fue Casa de Maximiano y María Sánchez
23. Casa de José Luis y Rosita Pacheco
24. Casa de Eduardo y Dorotea Durán
    Después fue Casa de Melitor y Octaviana Durán

25. Casa Literaria fundada en 1903
    Después fue Tienda y Casa de Raimoncito y Diana Fernández
    Después fue Tesoro y Joyas Casa Lee Corazón
26. Casa de Almindrey y Tomás Córdova
27. Después fue Casa de Bartolo y Carlota Martínez
28. Casa de José y Eleonor Córdova
    Casa de Juan y Adam Sánchez
29. Casa de José Dionicio y Casimira Córdova
30. Casa de Pedro y Emilia Sierra
31. Después fue Casa Flossan Zakary
    Después fue Tienda y Casa de la familia Trujillo
    También fue Estafeta manejada por Celestino Sandoval
    Después fue Casa y Estudio de Los Santeros (hippies)
32. Después allí vivió Horacio y Claudina Delgado
    Después fue Antonia y Juanita Trujillo
    Después fue Casa y Club Gay Nuestro de Gil y Helen Corbella
    Después fue Tienda Tenterday's
    Después fue Woman Inn The Bistro
33. Casa de Andrés y Margarita Martínez
    Los cuartos de atrás estaban arrentados a Melitón y Ora Chase
    Después en esos mismos cuartos vivían Amador y Fabiola Trujillo
34. Estafeta
35. Tienda de George y Jessie Mae Chase
    Después fue Colegio Goddard West
    Después fue Dormitorio Webb?yn
    Después fue Thomasville Snow-Montoisn
36. Casa de Lucas y Trinidad Pacheco
37. American Legion Hall
38. Noria de Laguerda Pacheco
    Después estaba la tienda de la Tienda de Levbino y Betty Martínez
    La Tienda de Luis y Franchiquita Cisneros se re-estableció al lado
    del sitio también
39. Salón de baile Casa y Estafeta de Rosendo y Aurelia Fernández
40. Después fue Salón de Arroyo Seco
41. Casa de Amarante y Adelina Vigil
    Después fue Casa de Fermín e Irene Torres
    Después fue Casa de Feliz y Frances Archuleta
    Después fue Casa de Leroy y Diana Apodaca
42. Casa de Emilio y Junalia Mares
43. Después fue Casa de José de la Luz y Erolita Mares
44. Casa de Gumerco y Juanita Gonzáles
    Después allí vivían Juana y Felis Ortiz
    Sitio de Estafeta y Escuela
45. Después fue Casa de Bernabé y Victoriana Gonzáles
    Después fue Casa y Palomar de Antonio Mendoza
    Después fue Casa que compraba por Luis O. y Berniza Torres
46. Casa de Modesto y Cleofes Medina
47. Casa de Pablo y Molly Pacheco
48. Casa de Amarante y Enriqua Valencia
    Después allí vivían Florindo y Amalia Martínez
    Después fue Casa de Juan y Julianita Gonzáles
    Casa de Emilia y Leocadia Valencia
49. Casa de Eutiquio y Susie Abeyta
    Después fue Casa de Maclovio y Soldana Martínez
50. Tienda de Ramón Martínez
    Después fue Tienda de Jesús Valdez
    Después fue Castillo Remby

Mapa hecho por **Larry Torres**
de dibujos y memorias de sus padres
Fermín Torres y Irene Márquez de Torres

Pueblo has denied exist in other cases.

Río Lucero water flows across the Tenorio Tract through the main Lucero Ditch, and across Arroyo Seco Creek where the waters are mixed by an elaborate gate. Diversions take water also to the Pueblo's Tenorio Tract and to El Prado. The Arroyo Seco flow is then redirected into the various lateral ditches that drain generally westerly and then to the southwest through El Prado and finally back to the Río Grande. The elevation drops approximately 300 feet from the mixing gate near El Salto Road to service the land in the Seco area.[32]

The Mexican-American War which began in March 1846, created additional problems in resolving land and water conflicts. A central provision of the Treaty of Guadalupe Hidalgo of 1848, which was supposed to end the War, involved the legal recognition of Spanish and Mexican land grants. The effect of this Treaty is still debated today after 150 years.[33] The agreement between two warring nations granted American citizenship to Spanish and Mexican citizens who lived in the areas taken by the United States. American citizens who had moved into New Mexico prior to the American victory, became citizens by birth. To implement the property rights promised by this national contract Congress created the Office of Surveyor General, which was empowered to investigate claims under the land grant system.

Eventually, a Court of Private Land Claims was created. Although a Spanish or Mexican land grant was recognized by the United States as a valid claim, it still had to be proven to exist according to the United States Supreme Court. The process has been slow. Filings in Congress by New Mexican Congressional Representatives in 1998 are intended to finally end public land title disputes in a speedy format.

The Land Court required proof of title by a writing which sometimes was lost or destroyed. Some pre-1680 documentation had been destroyed during the Pueblo Rebellion. Recording of titles with the county clerk was not yet an established procedure. Proof of continued physical possession of the property in question, therefore, became a very important issue. Claims that unscrupulous officials had intentionally destroyed documentation to steal the land have been commonly made.

Heirs of Antonio Martínez, who were still living on the Martínez Grant despite the courtroom warfare between the Sanches and Martín clans and their claims under the overlapping Antonio Martín land grant, successfully obtained a decree in 1892 from the United States Land Court validating the earlier 1716 Antonio Martínez Grant after a fifteen year legal wrangle.[34] The Grant was patented (a government deed issued) May 8, 1896.[35]

Court papers do not reflect objections by the Sanches heirs or by the Pueblo which had purchased the Martín interest or that they even knew what was happening. The record does not reflect that either of the families holding competing claims really paid much attention to each other. Silence is often an indication of lack of knowledge.

Following the court decree, Arthur R. Manby, a sociopathic Englishman, who previously had lived on the Maxwell Land Grant near Ratón, New Mexico, began to acquire large tracts of the newly validated Martínez Grant at tax sales and through private transactions with Martínez heirs in need of cash. Manby ultimately acquired substantially all of the interest of the Martínez heirs, assisted by a local attorney who also claimed to be a Martínez heir.[36]

Manby swindled investors between the years 1900 and 1909, including his 16-year-old wife's family. Finally, he lost the land grant in a receiver's sale in 1919. Ten years later on July 4, 1929, after having been divorced from his youthful spouse and living apparently alone except for his dog, Lobo, he was found beheaded and partially devoured by the faithful canine in his Taos hacienda that is now home to the Taos Art Association. The perpetrators were never legally identified and some question remains whether the headless body was that of Manby.[37]

Although Manby owned almost 61,000 acres of land around Arroyo Seco, he never lived in the community. He seems to have done a great deal of traveling. Divorce papers filed in Elbert County, Colorado, refer to claims of spousal abuse made by his young wife occurring in Trinidad, Colorado.

Manby was successful in establishing his legal title to

the 1716 Martínez Grant before the New Mexico Supreme Court in 1918 and 1921.[39] Not affected by the legal decree were both the Tenorio Tract that had been sold to the Pueblo by the Martín family and the claims of certain Spanish ranchers and farmers who held actual possession of the lands adversely to his claims in Arroyo Seco based on their claims under other overlapping land grants.

The earlier 1918 decision which also quieted title to the Martínez Grant tract in Manby was re-confirmed by the Supreme Court of New Mexico in the 1977 Ortiz case initiated by the Taos Pueblo.[40] The Taos Pueblo won a federal case in 1930 involving its claimed ownership of the Tenorio Tract which it had purchased from the Antonio Martín heirs.[41] Even though the 1716 Martínez Grant had been determined by a United States Court to be the valid grant, the Pueblo prevailed in its argument that it owned the Tenorio Tract (which logically should have no validity because the Martín Grant on which it was based had occurred later in time).

Accompanying this tract were the water, buildings built by the Arroyo Seco residents south of the creek, and irrigated lands constructed by the Hispanic farmers and ranchers who had occupied the south side of Arroyo Seco Creek for years based on the Martínez Grant title claim. The Seco farmers were forced to vacate in 1934. The United States paid the villagers $42,915 for their claims.[42]

The court's decision to uphold the Pueblo claim to the Tenorio Tract not only created hardship, it fathered a lasting viewpoint held by residents of Arroyo Seco who work the land that different standards of justice exist where the Pueblo is concerned. On the other hand, the Pueblo, which has also complained of multiple standards of justice, seems to have learned how to effectively and successfully operate within the United States judicial system.[43]

The legal decisions upholding the Pueblo's rights to the Tenorio Tract meant that the headgate to the Río Lucero Ditch, the Acequia Madre, which was located on Pueblo land, would be controlled by the Pueblo and that its permission would be required to maintain parts of the ditch situated on the Pueblo. The Pueblo fenced to the center of the Arroyo Seco Creek. That also meant a new road to Taos (State 150) would have to be constructed a few feet south of

Arroyo Seco Creek from Arroyo Seco to its intersection with State Road 230. It was unpaved and often impassable. Since the Pueblo claimed that its ownership extended to the middle of the creek, thereby claiming the road location and it would receive another payment for the land on which the road was located. Other roads throughout the land adjacent to or nearby the Pueblo in Taos were also claimed and settlements effected to clear the title. Claims to the lands near El Salto have been denied, however.

LAW BOOKS REPLACE BULLETS IN RESOLVING CONFLICTS

NUESTRA SEÑORA DE DOLORES, 1954
(circa 1830)
Holy Trinity Parish Archives, Photographer Unknown

NUESTRA SEÑORA DE DOLORES, 1954
(circa 1830)
Holy Trinity Parish Archives, Photographer Unknown

IV

SURVIVAL AND CHANGE
IN THE
20TH CENTURY

In the earliest times, the Arroyo Seco torreón was a place of safety and community refuge. It was probably occupied from 1740 to 1790 according to Jeffrey Boyer's archeological studies.[44] Pre-1680 structures were probably destroyed by victorious Pueblo warriors during the first Revolt. The tower was constructed in a strategic location on a high plateau near El Salto so that farmers could observe the Taos Valley for hundreds of miles to the west. It could well have been used to plot the movement of the night skies which reliably predicted planting and harvest times.

When the tower no longer was used for its primary function of defense, Boyer notes that its stone blocks were thrown into gullies to slow soil erosion. The location of the torreón is now a place of study and it serves to generate speculation on the survival culture of Arroyo Seco. Scientific evaluations of the tower remains have provided evidence in water disputes between the village and the Pueblo. Thus, its usefulness is not over.

Before the Treaty of Guadalupe Hidalgo, Seco was a Spanish community in a Spanish world which tolerated few foreigners. After Mexican Independence tolerance was extended to trappers and traders such as St. Vrain, Kit Carson, and the Bent brothers because they contributed to the economic well being of the area. Carson and Bent, who was killed in the 1847 conflict after being appointed military governor, were brothers-in-law having married well-to-do Spanish sisters sur-named Jaramillo. Even though the political world changed with the Treaty of Guadeloupe Hidalgo, this remote village retained its Spanish character and it remained on its own time.

The Treaty did not change the frequency of the periodic attacks of the Apache, Ute and Commanche Indian Tribes. Those conflicts were carried on with great abandon. Nomadic tribes continued warfare with the Pueblos, the Spanish and the Americans. Colonel E.V. Sumner wrote the Secretary of War in 1852 making a semi-serious proposal to give New Mexico back to Mexico.[45]

Most relationships did not change at the stroke of a legal pen. The grandiose schemes of A. R. Manby, who dreamed of developing the Martínez Land Grant, also failed to change the Seco character. Arroyo Seco remained agrarian, deeply religious, family based, and culturally conservative. These qualities continue. It took German imperialism in Europe during the mid-20th century to catalyze change in Arroyo Seco.

Following World War II and the passage of over one hundred years under the Treaty, a small number of Anglo settlers moved into Arroyo Seco. Frank Waters, a native of Colorado, part Cheyenne Indian and complete historian, acquired his home on El Salto Road from a descendant of the Antonio Martínez family. He lived there until his death in June 1995. His home and its lands have been preserved in the Taos Land Trust. A foundation, the Frank Waters Foundation, was established to encourage literary art. Barbara Waters his wife, also an author, still lives in the home and carries on the work of the Foundation.

Waters' writings which were both mystical and romantic sought to understand and then to explain the distinctly northern New Mexican point of view. His treatment of the Pueblo Indian culture created a narrow (and sometimes precarious) bridge between the Spanish residents and their Indian neighbors. Children who lived next to Water's home reportedly peeked through the fence to watch Indians dance at the Waters' residence.[46]

Paintings and photographs of other artists portrayed the isolation and hardship of the Taos Valley. Waters reminded his readers how it survived. He wrote about the survivors in a land that had continually tested and challenged survival. When Waters arrived in Arroyo Seco, schools frequently used the Spanish language as the primary language and trips to Taos were few and far between.[47] Today, knowledge of fluent Spanish by Hispanic children, may be the exception rather than the rule. Many residents did not have a truck when Waters moved to Seco. Pickups were loaded with children headed to the carnival and the fiestas in Taos in the summer. Except for bus trips to school, this was the only contact with the big city.

Seco had begun to lose population since there was little work for the newly returning veterans of the Second World War other than subsistence farming. Viable economic opportunities close to home dwindled with the loss of arable land despite attempts to create home industry in Arroyo Seco. Members of the community sought opportunities in other states, including Colorado, to support their families.

Then in the early part of the 1950's, there emerged a fledgling ski industry which depended upon snow for its survival. It became another user of water. The arrival of the skiing business became a new test for Seco and it threatened the community's isolation which had been its key to continued life. The ski valley became a competitor for resources, a user of the roads and a consumer of space and land, but it also provided work and brought new economic opportunities.

LA SANTÍSIMA TRINIDAD CHURCH, MARCH 31, 1996
Larry Torres Archives, Photograph by Te Zins

The community's adaptive skills were put to a new test. In the end, Seco traditions continued.

On Passion Sunday (Palm Sunday), March 31, 1996, the partially restored 1834 La Santísima Trinidad Church was blessed by a mixed congregation comprised of original families and newer members who had moved into Seco during the last few decades. The congregation marched from the Old Church along the county road in traditional procession to the New Church, led by Los

LA SANTÍSIMA TRINIDAD CHURCH, BEING REOCCUPIED ON PALM SUNDAY MARCH 31, 1996

Larry Torres Archives, Photograph by Te Zins

Hermanos of the nearby morada, singing traditional Penitente alabados (hymns).

Skiers, hoping to capture the last snow of an otherwise unusually dry 1996 season at Taos Ski Valley, had to patiently wait on the road in their cars while the procession slowly wound its way through the village. A deputy sheriff kept watch to assure the safety of the procession. The new ways grudgingly but respectfully gave way to the old and to another time.

A SKIER'S CROSS

V

THE SKIING COMMUNITY CONTRIBUTES TO CHANGE

The original European settlers of Arroyo Seco spoke Castillian Spanish and immigrated from the province of Extremadura in Spain. Basque sheepherders from Northern Spain (who were separatist in Spain and spoke their own language) brought their shepherds' talents to Arroyo Seco traveling with the Franciscan missionaries whose objective was to establish Christianity thoughout New Spain and to convert the Pueblo Indians to the Christian faith. The Poem, La Raza, written by Pablo

TAOS SKI VALLEY

Quintana of Arroyo Seco appears as a postscript to this book. He begins, "They came up the Rio Grande Valley herding their sheep, goats and cattle. They were peaceful

Basque shepherds but traveled ready for battle." Quintana's lyrical story of life under El Salto is filled with emotion and the love that his family has for the land.

A Mestizo Mexican culture, which resulted from the intermarriage between the Spanish and southern Indian population, remained primarily in southern New Spain or Mexico as it became known (the name derived from the Mexica Indians (pronounced meh-chee-ka) also referred to as Aztec). The isolated northern regions of New Mexico remained a European Spanish community which tolerated French trappers and endured a French-clergy dominated Archdiocese. It is probably not too surprising, then, that in the middle 1950's a new European community would immigrate into Arroyo Seco to establish the Taos Ski Valley.

Ernie Blake's mother was Swiss but he was born in Germany. Blake, who was schooled in Switzerland, came to the United States in 1938. After rejection by the 10th Mountain Division, he succeeded in joining the United States Army. In 1955, the Twining Ski Corporation which Blake owned and controlled, inaugurated the Taos Ski Valley located in the Sangre de Cristo Mountains near Arroyo Seco and subsequently employed generations of Arroyo Seco and neighboring Valdez families.[48]

The skiing industry in Twining impacted Arroyo Seco with its construction, water use and operations. Jobs, sewage and increased traffic became issues which were addressed in political confrontations with local community organizations. A number of the Taos Ski Valley associates purchased property and built homes and businesses in the village and became new community members.

Jean and Dadou Mayer and their mother and father, Nicole and Charles immigrated from the Alsace-Lorraine, a northeastern province of France. In 1957, Blake, with the assistance of his associate, Al Rosen, convinced Jean Mayer, who had served with the U.S. Army in Garmisch, Austria, to come to the Taos Valley. In 1958 the Mayer family arrived in New Mexico and Jean Mayer built the St. Bernard Restaurant in Twining at the base of the first ski lift near the original Hondo Lodge. Jean Mayer is the technical director of skiing at the Taos Ski Valley and continues to operate the St. Bernard Restaurant.

Godie Schuetz was trained in the Swiss military and later taught in the U.S. Army during the Second World War. Schuetz came to the Taos Ski Valley in 1959 as a ski instructor and subsequently bought the Casa Córdova Restaurant in Arroyo Seco in 1965 turning that old local adobe restaurant into a nationally known location. His European style transformed the bar into a meeting place for business and politics. The century-plus old adobe hacienda became an important place of local employment. In the beginning Schuetz provided the largest individual village payroll. Many of his Swiss traditions coincided with those of his Spanish neighbors. Reflecting on the community, Schuetz recalled that he "knew not to impose his views on those around him if he intended to remain." Schuetz still lives in his adobe home in Arroyo Seco.

Other German, Swiss, and French entrepreneurs and employees came to the Hondo Valley and with the assistance of people from Seco and the Taos Pueblo helped Ernie Blake build and operate the Taos Ski Area. European customs and traditions found a new home in Arroyo Seco. Loved or hated at the time, (and sometimes embattled), the Ernie Blake dream to build a major skiing resort became reality.

Blake died in 1989, 35 years after his initial purchase of the mountainside in the canyon. His family in a public/private partnership with the U. S. Forest Service has continued to build and improve the Taos Ski Valley, its facilities, hotels and amenities. Other participants in the project include not only the Mayers, the Brownell's, but also several generations of Seco families who continue to work at the ski valley. The new skiing industry and culture arrived in time to supplement the local agrarian economy which was unable to sustain the historic population with its post-war changes.

To drive to the Taos Ski Valley by the most direct route, a skier must cruise slowly through Arroyo Seco, negotiate its several ninety-degree turns and follow Highway 150 north approximately one mile where it again turns abruptly to the right (the east). Drivers who miss the turn can find themselves in the acequia which is below the wall of the rim or, in a worse condition, in the Hondo River 100 feet below.

The new canyon road, built in 1971, passes by the

Los Altos subdivision created in 1989 by Rick and Sally Edelman from farming fields and catch ponds. Leo Valencia's old gas station dangles off the Hondo rim on the north and is sometimes used for residential purposes or an occasional motion picture set.

The road winds its way 12 miles up the Hondo Canyon following the Rio Hondo, past camp grounds bearing names such as Cuchilla del Medio and trails that ascend steeply to the north to wind their way to Red River. The old gold mining town of Amizette was named in 1893 for the first Anglo woman to claim to have followed the dirt trail up the canyon.[49] Amizette is now the location of several European style lodges and hot tubs. Formerly a pioneer hotel site and short-lived mining area, Amizette is a mile away from the skiing area. It was incorporated into the newly created municipality called Taos Ski Valley in 1966.

The river and road finally end at the box canyon site of the former Hondo Lodge in Twining that served as the base of the ski area when Blake constructed it in 1954. The mining town of Twining emerged when gold and copper were found in paying quantities in 1895. About 200 people lived in this community until its smelter froze - never to smelt again.[50]

The Brownell's Thunderbird, Jean Mayer's St. Bernard and the Snakedance Hotels, among others, now greet skiers in what used to be a mining boomtown. In 1996, one hundred years after mining boom and bust, the ski valley experienced an unusually dry winter season that particularly affected Arroyo Seco's spring irrigation. In February 1996, following several heavy snows which saved the TSV season, Tim Harter, the popular owner of Tim's Stray Dog Cantina, tragically died in an avalanche on Kachina Peak having just purchased The Chile Connection Restaurant situated on the road to Seco. Tim's Chile Connection is still operated by his wife, Laurie Harter.

Several months later, part of the original Edelweiss Hotel built by Dadou Mayer, but recently sold to new owners, burned to the ground. Tragically one of the new proprietors of this historic lodge who had been an original Taos Ski Valley town council member was killed within a few months in a bicycling accident in Taos.

During the 60's which were the formative years of the Taos Ski Valley, Charles and Nicole Mayer acquired several acres of farmland owned by a local family less than one-half mile from the village. Jean Mayer built a home with his wife, Sally, on part of the property in 1977. Eleven years later Dadou Mayer bought the house and established a bed and breakfast inn which he named, Salsa del Salto.

Dadou Mayer, became a member of the local acequia organization in order to receive irrigation water from the ditch. He says that he attended its periodic meetings where water allocations were determined and quickly learned that a failure to actively participate could mean irrigation water is not made available to his property. The need for water insured that the traditional values community would be continued.

INSIDE OF LA SANTÍSIMA TRINIDAD CHURCH, ARROYO SECO 1998
Photographed by George Marcek

VI

THE CHURCH AND PENITENTE BROTHERHOOD SUSTAIN THE COMMUNITY FOR TWO HUNDRED YEARS

The history of religious activity in Arroyo Seco involves, in part, the story of the Franciscan Order in New Mexico, the impact of the appointment of a series of French Archbishops to the Roman Catholic Archdiocese of Santa Fe and the emergence of the lay religious fraternity known as the Penitentes (La Fraternidad Piadosa de Nuestro Padre Jesús Nazareno). Saint Francis of Assisi, the founder of the Franciscan Order, was a 12th Century Italian. His vow of poverty and celibacy followed a short, but apparently active, period of self-indulgence.

Spanish priests and lay brethren led their secular

OLD PENITENTE MORADA IN VALDEZ

followers into the northern regions of New Mexico founding missions along the way. The goals of the Franciscans diverged from those of the Conquistadors. The riches of the fabled cities of Cibola drew the expeditionary forces in the beginning. The conversion of Indians became the primary goal of the Spanish clergy led by Franciscan Friars when gold could not be found in New Mexico. To accomplish this, the Franciscans built mission churches throughout their jurisdiction (custody.)

Blanche Grant reported that three Taos mission churches were possibly built in the Taos Pueblo of which the first two were constructed under the direction of Franciscan priests. Grant suggests that the first such mission was constructed in 1617 by Friar Pedro de Miranda 19 years after the Oñate expedition.[51] Miranda was later killed in 1639 during one of several conflicts between the Taos Pueblo residents and the Spanish. The 1680 Pueblo Revolt resulted in the deaths of two Franciscan Friars at the Taos Pueblo. Taos Friar Antonio Carbonel was martyred in 1696 along with other Franciscan priests while trying to retreat to Santa Fe. A second Taos Pueblo church may have been built after the 1680 Revolt. The second church stood until 1847 when the Army of the United States blew it apart with howitzer cannonades. The third and last church currently serves the Pueblo.

The license to build the Arroyo Seco Mission Church issued in 1826 after Mexican Independence. Bishop Zubiría of Durango, Mexico is said to have only visited New Mexico three times during a 20-year period. His reluctance to travel north may have evidenced the church's predominate interest in conversion of Indians versus its administration of the diocese, or it may simply reflect the long distances that existed and the lack of speedy and comfortable transportation.

Consecration of the nearby Valdez Mission occurred in 1842 after its earlier construction in 1826. Arroyo Hondo's mission which is now part of the Arroyo Seco Parish originates from 1834. It was in Hondo that Padre Martínez, defrocked eventually by Vicar Machebeuf, frequently conducted religious services. Hondo was its own parish from 1850 to 1866. The mission of San Francisco de Asís in Ranchos de Taos dates from 1815. The only church located on the original Martínez Land Grant after the American shells destroyed the church of San Jerónimo at the Taos Pueblo was La Santísima Trinidad Church in Seco. It had been finished one year after the Hondo mission and was attached to the Taos Parish. Both the Hondo mission and the Valdez mission are located on the Hondo Grant.

Franciscans, whose Order was governed from Spain, were not expelled from New Mexico after secularization of the New Mexican missions that resulted from the Mexican government's order directing Spaniards to leave Mexico.[52] Rather, the Franciscans simply stayed and died and were not replaced. The last Franciscan to be appointed by Bishop Zubiriá arrived in 1845 and succumbed in 1848. With his death came the end of Franciscanism in the 19th Century.

La Santísima Trinidad Church in Arroyo Seco left the Taos Parish as a mission to become its own parish of The Holy Trinity in 1946. Father Elmer L. Niemeyer, an assistant at Our Lady of Guadalupe in Taos was assigned to Holy Trinity until 1952. Niemeyer was an Anglo[53] who was appointed to lead a church that was still rooted in a Spanish religious world. His attempts to better the economic life of villagers were reportedly met first with distrust and then with appreciative approval. Colonial Spanish furniture began to be produced in Arroyo Seco as an industry due to his efforts. Plans to restart a woodworking project in the Seco Elementary School which has been replaced with a new elementary school (Arroyos del Norte) are being made by Father Vincent Chávez, the current parish priest and in a line of 20 priests appointed to lead the parish since parish status was achieved.

Neimeyer died in February 1997. Neimeyer had been responsible for filming the interiors and exteriors of the village churches of Arroyo Seco, Arroyo Hondo, Valdez and others.[54] Neimeyer's foreword-looking term as the priest of the Old Church in Arroyo Seco has provided the restorers of the Old Church with an accurate record of its condition 50 years ago.

While the church has served an important and central role in providing for 19th and 20th century survival, dogmatic disputes or personality disputes caused the general New Mexican laity to look beyond a French dominated religious organization during the early 19th century. Due in part to the independent and self-sufficient character of New Mexican Hispanic pioneers, an active Penitente movement modeled in part from Orders found in Europe emerged with characteristics which are unique to northern New Mexico and Southern Colorado. The Order's role included social, political, and communal activities as well as spiritual support and nourishment.

The Penitente organization was important to the sustainability of the Arroyo Seco community given the geographic, religious, and cultural isolation of the village. The Brotherhood was essentially forbidden to practice their doctrine for decades following orders by Catholic Archbishop Jean Baptiste Salpointe in 1892 who compared Los Penitentes to Masons whose secret society had been condemned by the Catholic Church and was deemed abhorrent.[55]

The fraternity survived even though its membership declined following a period of official disapproval. Tragically, many of the Order's religious icons, *Santos*, painted *Retablos* and carved *Bultos* created by gifted 19th century artists were removed from moradas, sold or given away.

A PAINTED RETABLO

Many pieces originating from the moradas of Arroyo Hondo, for example, are on display at the Taylor Museum in Colorado Springs, Colorado, and are depicted in *Arroyo Hondo, The Folk Art of A New Mexican Village*, Robert L. Shalkop, published by The Taylor Museum of the Colorado Springs Fine Arts Center in 1969. This famous museum has, to its credit, had much to do with the rejuvenation of the folk art form exemplified by its *Santos* collection. In a Spanish and Indian Market held during June, 1998, in Colorado Springs, not less than 10 exhibitors were

Santeros-artists who had painted or carved beautiful and original sacred folk art from New Mexico and Colorado.

The Penitente existence was reconciled with and approved by Archbishop Edwin V. Byrne on January 27, 1947. The sanction allowed the Brothers to bring their organization back into the open. Byrne granted the Order the Church's blessing and protection provided that the Order proceed with moderation and under supervision of the Archdiocese. It was mandated to

A CARVED BULTO C. LATE 1700'S DE LA SANTÍSIMA TRINIDAD DE LA IGLESIA VIEJA BY JOSE RAFAEL ARAGÓN
Larry Torris Archives

refrain from political activity which had been one of the Brotherhood's important functions. The demise of political activity within the morada resulted in greater emphasis being placed on local party political organization and its administration.

While other independent moradas became inactive due to lack of resolve or the physical deterioration of the meeting place, the 1870 Arroyo Seco morada, from all public observations, seems to have flourished and, perhaps, grown. Each year during Lent, the Hermanos of the Arroyo Seco morada have conducted their public procession and Good Friday-Easter related services in conjunction with the religious activi-

SAN CRISTOBAL SANTO
Santos Documentation Project
Santa Fe Council for the Arts
Photograph by Jack Parsons, 1987

ties at Holy Trinity Parish.[56] Today the organizations appear to coordinate activities and work together to solve many social and doctrinal concerns.

THE SACRED HEART LEAGUE
IS IMPORTANT IN ARROYO SECO

VII

LOCAL ORGANIZATIONS HELP TO PRESERVE THE VILLAGE IDENTITY

Strong family traditions and a seeming unending progression of church based activities have had a great deal to do with Arroyo Seco retaining its separate identity for several centuries. As the village evolved into each new century various new organizations emerged which further enabled the community to survive and to cope with change. Arroyo Seco developed both formal and informal means of regulating its social behavior.

Government

During the Conquest an encomendero was granted a large tract of land and given the authority to require Indians to work the land.[57] Using this mechanism of power the Spanish Crown was able to control - at least in concept - the wide ranging province of New Mexico. The Spanish encomienda provided security for communal roots to set. The Spanish King acted through his designated chief located in Mexico City of New Spain who was the Viceroy. This official interacted with the Governor or Captain-General of the Kingdom of New Mexico as well as other governors and the persons possessing the various encomiendas.

Always along side the Governor and sometimes feuding

with him was the Franciscan representative whose role it was to convert the pagan native cultures and gather souls. Over time these souls provided a useful pool of labor to build magnificent missions and tend gardens for the Franciscan friars. The Franciscan custody was ruled from Spain, as well.

As Spanish rural villages developed, an alcalde who was both judge and mayor, was elected to represent legal authority within the village. The alcalde was a peoples' officer and his decisions were based on ethical considerations more than written laws.[58] The Antonio Martín case involving the partition of Seco lands which was resolved in 1826 reflects that a circuit riding alcalde from the village of El Prado, located between Arroyo Seco and Taos, exercised jurisdiction in Arroyo Seco relating to the land title controversy. His decision is a good example of how the alcalde system functioned during the early 19th century.

Following the American conquest in 1846, Stephen Watts Kearny, was appointed to the position of military governor by the Secretary of War and President. He was followed by Charles Bent who was killed in Taos during the 1847 revolt. The government functioned from Santa Fe using the same building facilities previously used by the Spanish, the indigenous Pueblo government which followed the Revolt in 1680 and the Mexican Governor after 1821. A series of replacement military governors followed Bent until the Treaty of Guadalupe Hidalgo was finally approved and New Mexico was granted Territorial status by Congress. A Territorial Government was elected in 1851 by males who had elected American citizenship. Following Anglo tradition an elective civil government was organized by white males which included Hispanic citizens who had sworn allegiance to the American system.

The government included the full panoply of Territorial and local positions of power. A Territorial legislature was elected in which Padre Antonio Martínez honorably served as its first Council President.[59] During 1912 New Mexico finally achieved Statehood after many unsuccessful attempts (fifty statehood bills had been proposed in sixty years) which had been derailed by national considerations as well as concerns over local issues. Slavery and fear of the status of the native Indian cultures whose sovereignty was in question overshadowed the statehood discussion. The Indian Wars with the Apache and then the Navajo culminated in a vague and undefined Indian policy which characterized Territorial politics for years.[60]

At the local level, the Taos County Sheriff maintains peace in Arroyo Seco and sometimes jails the accused. Then it is up to local judges, juries and prosecutors to apply the law. Trials for Seco transgressors take place in Taos. The original County Court House was located on the Taos Plaza. It now functions as art galleries. The newer County facilities are located further south on Paseo del Pueblo Sur at the cross street, Albright. In earlier times, Seco had a tendency of dealing with its own behavior problems without involving the Sheriff and, to a lesser extent, this practice continues.

Acequia Commission

Following the predominating influence of the Church, the acequia organization which regulated irrigation from the series of ditches that appear throughout Arroyo Seco was the next most important system regulating behavior in this agrarian community. Democratically elected acequia commissions implement policy for the acequia membership which collectively comprise the legally established body. The acequia organization and its operation was established by state law. Parciantes (voting members) currently vote by representation without regard to the amount of land they own. This rule has been contested in one recent lawsuit in Taos County in which a large landowner argued

ACEQUIAS ARE THE VEINS THAT FEED OUR FIELDS, OUR LIVE STOCK AND GIVE US ALL LIFE TO OUR DESERT WAY OF LIVING

that since he owned the majority of the land irrigated by the ditch, he should have voting rights commensurate to his holdings. The parciante lost the case.

Acequia meetings in Arroyo Seco are conducted partially in the Spanish language. Non-Hispanic members must learn the necessary traditional process to gain their share of the ditch flow. Spring cleaning of ditches requires physical participation of persons claiming water rights or a designated substitute. Ditch duties are formally announced and appear in the newspaper and in other forms of public announcement.

The mayordomo (ditch-boss) marks in his notebook who will receive water from the ditch and when it will be delivered. If a ditch bank is cut (usually by the timeworn hoe) to allow the water to flood the adjacent field, and the ditch is not closed at the agreed time, a fine is levied against the offending user by the mayordomo. The fine that is charged for improper water use is intended to remind the user of his duty to the next irrigator below him. The custom is to supply a fair share of water to the neighbor. The mayordomo is in charge for a year. He is elected by the members of the ditch association. Acequia traditions, including the spring cleaning duty, are among the oldest in New Mexico. They recall the Moorish customs imported from Spain by Seco's ancestors.

Political Organization

Even though Arroyo Seco maintains a separate identity as a village both physically due to its location and by tradition, it has not been legally incorporated. In contrast the newer Taos Ski Valley petitioned for its own government during the 1990's and elected its own council in 1996 which is responsible for local planning and community matters. Seco is governed locally by the Taos County Commission. The Taos Sheriff and State Police provide security as personnel permit. The County Sheriff is primarily responsible to keep the peace in Arroyo Seco. Due to the size of Taos County, the Sheriff rotates certain designated duties with the State Police.

Civil duties, such as serving lawsuit papers, remain in

the Sheriff's office.   Currently the Sheriff administers 16 deputies and an undersheriff.   The relatively low budget for security when compared to urban population centers coupled with the large size of Taos County and the isolation of Arroyo Seco places a premium on local cooperation in law enforcement.   Every four years, a new sheriff is elected. Partisan politics dictates the winner.

Fire protection is provided by the Hondo-Seco Volunteer Fire Department which was created in 1977 to provide local organized fire protection where none had previously existed. Recent vandalism to fire department facilities has generated new community concern for its self-protection. Annually the volunteers canvas the area that they serve for financial support. Political activity transcends many of the activities in Arroyo Seco.   Greater emphasis was placed on partisan political organization after Penitente political activities were curtailed by the Archdiocese. The local party precinct leadership who recommend appointive work, achieved substantial status and increased power and are important positions in organized political life. The emergence of the Green Party, an environmentalist based organization, has changed the balance of power.   In 1998 they drew between 4% to 5% of the vote which can result in importance greater than raw numbers in a close race.

Taos County is culturally conservative by nature yet it has had a long history of supporting the Democratic Party which is considered to be more liberal on the political charts. Strongholds of Republican (conservative) sentiment exist at all levels, however. New Mexico has voted a split ticket in recent times. The State Legislature currently consists of a Democratic   majority sometimes offsetting Republican Governors who tend to gain their strength from the southern part of the state. Presently, Senator Peter Domenici is the Republican U.S. Senator and Jeff Bingaman, the Democrat, is his counterpart in the U..S. Senate.   Former United States Congressman Bill Richardson, a Democrat, was appointed to President Bill Clinton's cabinet and has served as the U.S. Representative to the United Nations. 1998 elections again reflected the split in political philosophy between the northern and southern ends of the state.

There are several bosses or mayordomos in Arroyo

Seco. The parish priest is certainly an important and highly respected person having substantial influence. From among the laity, individuals hold honorary positions for special events. Various individuals are asked to lead committees or task groups and then the incumbent changes. There are different bosses for different functions such as the domestic water system, the acequia, the planning association, church committees and the Penitente Brotherhood.

Each is important in their own organization and respected as a leader for that group.

Schools

Curriculum, manner of instruction and the condition and design of facilities rank at the top of the list of local school concerns. The construction of a new elementary school, Arroyos del Norte Elementary on the Hondo-Seco Road directed by the Taos Municipal School Board has not been without difficulty. 215 students (kindergarten through fifth grade) from Arroyo Seco, Arroyo Hondo, Des Montes and Valdez occupied the new

NEW ARROYO HONDO / ARROYO SECO ELEMENTARY SCHOOL

school on August 30, 1998, following a delay required by building code issues.

Already, modular temporary structures have revised the $8,000,000 campus plan. The clustered school facility will redistribute children to the west side of Arroyo Seco instead of to its core. Traffic

NEW ARROYO HONDO / ARROYO SECO ELEMENTARY SCHOOL

along the narrow Hondo-Seco Road, safety issues and home schooling compete with neighborhood reactions to the color scheme chosen for the school's metal-sided gymnasium. A subject of ongoing debate is the disparate architecture of the temporary classrooms that were placed in front of the porticos joining permanent southwestern style buildings to each other. The new school will share its principal with Enos Garcia Elementary in Taos. A head-teacher is expected to handle various administrative duties which, unfortunately, removes her from the classroom from time to time. Assisting the teachers and administration is an active Parent-Teachers Organization.

Questions related to education continue to compete with facility issues now that the building has been largely completed. Student discipline will be tested by mixing historically separate school groups. Library improvements are needed. All children who arrive at school before a specified time are provided free breakfast in the morning. Lunches continue to be moderately priced and are free to some students.

Traditional Hispanic meals which were appreciated by most of the students and parents alike have been replaced by a diet based on food groups. Apparently, the expenditure of $8 million did not include a provision for swing equipment in the playground. With the occupation of the Arroyos del Norte school the old elementary school building in Arroyo Seco has become

OLD ARROYO SECO SCHOOL WAS BUILT AS A WPA CONTRUCTION PROJECT, CIRCA 1930'S
New Mexico Records Center & Archives
Photograph by Helen Green Blumenshein

available for community activities. The School Board leased the building to the County which will oversee its eventual reuse.

Long sought after as a community center, the old

school is in need of the same careful and detailed restoration as the Old Church. Father Chávez has proposed establishing woodworking instruction, as was sponsored by the late Father Niemeyer who opened a school for manufacturing Spanish colonial furniture. Depending on which entity falls heir to the old school, the possibility exists that another local governing board will be created with an additional agenda.

The new entity will be faced with financing the high cost of operating and maintaining the old school as a community project. The task of raising the necessary funds to pay for this next venture will require a concerted effort from the village similar to the process involved in the restoration of the Old Church. The recently abandoned elementary school was built during the 1930's as a Works Progress Administration Project. Buses for the high school in Taos met at the Seco Elementary School to pick up their passengers. Family pets were so used to the practice that at least one dog not only followed students to the bus but also was there, waiting, when the bus returned.

Commerce

A loosely organized group of businesses operating within Arroyo Seco has combined with other community

groups to offer new activities. The Spring Arts Festival promotes creativeness, history and the Seco character. The now Annual Fourth of July Parade has grown each year into an event that has involved all villagers. During the summer, the Seco Stroll seeks to

INDEPENDENCE DAY PARADE 1998

encourage tourism and visitors into the community during evening hours.

Because of the turnover in business in Seco, it is difficult to develop economic continuity. Terry Wolff, who assisted in the publication of this book, maintains a Web Site for the village through Gray Wolf Trading Co. of Taos. In the

Spring of 1997 he constructed a site for the village, thus thrusting the village into cyberspace. Other local businesses, including the Frank Waters Foundation and KRZA, the areas local community radio station have their own Web Sites which are maintained by Terry. It is hard to imagine this isolated village backdropped by Lucero Peak, dominated

PARADE GRAND MARSHALL, ED SANDOVAL
INDEPENDENCE DAY PARADE 1998

by El Salto, in a valley known for its mystery, to be now accessible to anyone in the world with a personal computer.

Land Use Planning

Within the last few decades various populist land use groups reflecting concern over growth and destruction of traditional land uses have organized to combat the changes taking place in Arroyo Seco and adjacent communities. In 1972 the Arroyo Hondo/Seco Development Corporation was formed, which operated for several years. It was responsible for material improvements to the joint communities including neighborhood recreation facilities.

During 1982 a special zoning district was proposed for the Hondo Valley to deal with the construction of a condominium development in Valdez. The community took sides and the dispute was referred to as The Condo Wars or The Valdez Condominium Wars in the newspaper. The zoning district was later ruled unconstitutional by the court and parts of the condominium development were never finished. A concrete skeleton of the unfinished structure is still visible from the Cuchilla Road. Protest signs are displayed at the Smithsonian Institute in Washington, D.C.

Newly arrived on the local political scene is the Arroyo Seco/Valdez Neighborhood Association. Formed in 1995 in response to a countywide land use planning initiative, it is one of 32 such neighborhood organizations which have struggled with formulating a master plan for future development within its jurisdiction. The Association maintains a line of communication with the County Planning Director. In 1997 a proposed use of farming land for a commercial candle factory near the Rim Road was defeated due to the objection of neighborhood activists and representatives. While sub-division issues are now determined based upon statewide standards, the local plan presents a vision statement which future planning commission recommendations and county commission decisions will probably try to follow.

In Arroyo Seco, sub-division problems often occur. Larger tracts of land once dedicated to farming have been sub-divided for residential development. One lot may now be sub-divided every five years, regardless of size. Special rules are provided for family transfers to protect the historic practice of dividing land in favor of children.[61]

Where land has become a commodity rather than a producer of food, pressure has mounted for small lot subdivisions which are designed to maximize returns. Land transactions taking place in the Arroyo Seco area of influence indicate that there are a substantial number of new owners who are dedicating their assets to preserve rather than divide the open spaces.

Taos County has few zoning rules which has resulted in a variety of uses and architecture. The county is zoned Rural Agricultural. The current land use plan regulates commercial enterprise, major development and steep slope development. The use of planned unit development which, in effect, micro manages land planning by the county, is out of the ordinary. In this respect, the Los Altos Subdivision which has been opposed by planning activists is unique to the area.

Land use in response to the dwindling agriculturally based economy and conversion to tourist-based enterprise presents the clearest current challenge to preservation of fields, open space, and the traditions of a farming and ranching heritage in Arroyo Seco during the next decade. Education regarding the need for traditional uses and open space must be high on any political agenda to gain credibility in Arroyo Seco.

VIII

AGRARIAN PRACTICES
MEET
NEW CHALLENGES

Subsistence farming simply means that farm production is consumed locally (usually on the farm that grew the corn or raised the sheep) rather than being sold elsewhere for money. This form of industry characterized Arroyo Seco's economy for almost 400 years until the evolution into tourism was catalyzed by World War II and then confirmed by the growth of the skiing business.

George I. Sánchez reported that in 1936 there were but 2200 farms in Taos County of which only half consisted of areas of 6 acres or fewer. Sanchez opined that the minimum optimum size of a farm in the county should be at least 35 acres. He stated that no more than five or six county farms encompassed 200 acres or larger. As families grew in numbers, farming land was divided among family members in smaller sized units.

Today this practice continues in Seco in traditional Spanish families. Even lots which have been identified for the construction of homes have become smaller because of the practice of family subdivision. The December 27, 1995, Proposed Vision Statement of the Arroyo Seco/Valdez Neighborhood Association proposed the goal of continuing and protecting the family land subdivision tradition.

In contrast to the practice of subdividing arable land,

the neighboring Pueblo emphasizes community use of its lands. Herds of buffalo and cattle which are privately owned range over separated pastures which are moved from place to place to avoid overgrazing. Individual plots are assigned to herds and their owners, much like the Forest Service, issues grazing permits.

Only through cooperative farming by Seco neighbors of the smaller individual parcels on the Spanish side of the Arroyo Seco Creek, have farmers been allowed to survive on the

Main Street Arroyo Seco, where the buffalo roam and the deer and tourists play (1994)
Photographer on the run and unknown
(film retrieved from remains of camera)

less than optimum acreage described by Sánchez. Experience has shown that large lot size as a predetermining factor of productivity is not necessarily a given truth where joint farming occurs. In times of need, the Seco harvest has been first allocated to widows and their children or elders from common stores - sometimes to the detriment of the family of the producing farmer.[62] Common farming by families, overcomes small land sizes. Nancy Quintana Carrasco has described common harvesting of grains and vegetables in the village.

The agricultural tradition is, after the Church, the strongest and most important activity. Some might reverse the priority. During Seco's formative period, every landowner who lived in the area worked the land and depended upon its produce to live. The Second World War depleted farms of their labor which were the male descendants of farmers who had depended upon the land for at least two hundred years. The advent of the Taos Ski Valley then created a new market for dirt and space that had become under utilized for farming due to the war. Real property became the subject of barter in the struggle for continued survival. Reacting to the transfer of farms to non-agricultural uses, traditionalists organized to oppose periodic development proposals permitting new uses. The organized opposition to change met with both success and failure.

The Taos Land Trust was established in 1991, in part due to a gift of a conservation easement by Frank and Barbara Waters whose home in Arroyo Seco is located on its historic creek. The Waters family donated an easement which prohibited development on their lands in perpetuity. In doing so Waters stated, We are not the owners of the land we occupy, nor its tenants, nor simply its caretakers. We are a part of the living earth itself.[63] Parishioners of the Holy Trinity Parish, the Healy Family of Arroyo Hondo, contributed seed money to the Trust through the M. A. Healy Family Foundation.

As of 1998, the Trust has accumulated over fifteen hundred acres of easement preserved lands of which 738 acres are working farmland. Fifteen conservation easements have been responsible for this historic portfolio. Donation of an easement typically allows the owner to continue his or her traditional use of the land while preventing urbanization.[64] The gifts of the easements can constitute charitable donations and permit the owner to apply for current deductions in income tax obligations.

The Trust sponsors fund raising ventures which benefit the lands that it seeks to protect. In 1998 the Trust hosted its sixth Art and Adventures auction which featured donations by local artists of original paintings, ceramics, jewelry and photography. A partnership in tradition, the Trust and the Art Community have joined local land use associations and private landowners to preserve lands which have been communally worked for over three hundred years.

While virtually every man was a farmer in the mid 1800's and depended upon his produce to support the family, in 1998 there are very few farmers and ranchers who depend upon their land as their sole source of livelihood. Several Seco farmers maintain large land producing areas. However, only a handful of families can be identified who currently make their entire living from farming or ranching without supplemental income. Almost everyone who owns a farm or a ranch in Arroyo Seco depends on second or third sources of income to live.

In the 19th Century, Taos and Mora Counties were referred to as the Grain Capital of the West.[65] Few buildings existed away from Arroyo Seco Creek. A 1939 aerial photograph depicts the Seco fields that produced food crops and the lateral acequia lines flowing to the southwest. Only three or four residential structures and barns can be identified outside of the village area and beyond Creek side.

In the unirrigated ranges of Arroyo Seco, sheep were allowed to graze under open range rules. A system of sharecropping in which the shepherd agreed to share his lamb crop with the owner of the land where the sheep were raised existed as a form of cooperative partnership between capital and labor. The arrangement was called El Partido.

Solitary living was mandatory for a shepherd. As a very young man, Fermín Torres was sent to southern Colorado by his family to guard his father's flock.[66] He remained alone almost a full year during which he was isolated from family and all other people. Fermín's only companions were his dog and the lambs for which he was responsible. Few farmers or ranchers sought the life of a shepherd. The religious irony is inescapable. Parents, attempting to convince their sons to continue school, sometimes offered their sons the alternative of a life of solitude with the flock. The proposal was considered a serious threat and it was extremely effective in evoking obedience.[67] That threat is no longer available in this new era.

There is no model of a 21st Century farm in Arroyo Seco. That is partially because there are few complete farms left. However, almost every landowner other than the few that own homes in the Los Altos subdivision, raises some form of livestock. As have other long lasting families, the Quintana family has lived in Seco for centuries.

Surrounding his hand-built home which includes a sweat bath reflecting Pablo's spiritual orientation, fences try to contain lambs, cattle, poultry, and his swine herd in their own corrals and pens. Mr. Lucky, the father hog to many lesser pigs, enjoys a lifestyle reserved usually for European royalty. At 1000 pounds, this patriarchal porker commands respect and attention. Pablo's various animals provide him a living which is sufficient for his needs. His approach to farming and life is undoubtedly envied by neighbors, whether native or newcomer, whose dream is to return to basic village values and lifestyle.

While life in Arroyo Seco seems, from the outside, to have avoided many of the traumatic disruptions that are evident in other parts of Taos County or in larger population centers in New Mexico, the changes for longtime residents are obvious and are both bad and good. Jobs and the ability to support young families usually override the nostalgia for the way it was.

Romantic memories of the how it used to be oftentimes are improved upon over time. Citizens of Arroyo Seco have observed the changes on a daily basis and may, in some cases, be part of the change. Persons who formerly resided in this village have been heard to express shock and distress at the transition that has taken place in Seco. These expressions of dismay evidence the fact that the romantic memory of what has been may have more reality than what really is or what really was.

LO QUE VIENE

History usually depends on the storyteller's point of view. Much that we hear is simply opinion and not fact. The modern word for opinion is spinning which means the story has been intentionally oriented toward a predisposed conclusion. The use of that phrase is severely overused. The further away in time that the fact has occurred, the less likely it is to have happened the way it is described. So even this story (short as it is) has to be judged by these rules. Hopefully we have not gone too far out in adopting as fact something that is really just a guess.

There is a lot of guessing, for example, about life that takes place in the Taos Pueblo if you are from the outside. While producing brilliant artists, writers and thinkers many of its important traditions are not described for the public. So they are not understood. We have the impression from Martiniano in *The Man Who Killed the Deer* written in 1942 by Frank Waters that spirit and spiritual forces play a major part in decision making in the Pueblo and there is nothing to indicate that anything has changed.

The Pueblo maintains its overall agenda based on a

unique political and social status which itself is a product of recent history. It can call on the power of the United States government or it can choose to remain aloof from the fray and stay very private. The Pueblo participates in wider community activities as in education, sports and politics, but its physical border is marked by a wire fence which clearly implies, Don't enter – unless invited.

It is private property, after all, purchased in part from the Martín family who were land grantees of a European king. Pueblo land collectively belongs to the Pueblo in its

"LA SANTISIMA TRINIDAD"
de
ARROYO SECO

tribal capacity which is not unlike property belonging to a business with several thousand shareholders.[68] Thus, in this respect it resembles a mainstream capital structure. Others might view that economy as the opposite. Point of view is important.

Arroyo Seco has no similar corporate characteristic and the village borders are marked by streams, valleys and mountains - not fences. While there are some few private locations which are mostly religious, the village is, for the most part, open and it invites inquiry. Seco was not attacked by the United States during Polk's War with Mexico although this incident does not appear to be as important to the

Pueblo as the killing of Acoma residents by Oñate.

While Seco village residents have been native for over 300 years, they were still not first in the area. That status belongs to the long gone pit dwellers who even preceded the Pueblo. Although profoundly spiritual, decisions in the village are based on criteria which tend to reflect European tradition and rationalism. In these ways, Seco is different from its Pueblo neighbor to the south.

Both of these survivors have lived on approximately the same ground, side by side, separated by a small creek that is larger in importance than its actual proportion. These neighbors have experienced many of the same hardships of weather, have suffered from the difficulties of a subsistence economy and the changes and losses brought about by World Wars in Europe. Despite these similarities, there is a continuing competition for the use of defined natural resources.

Aggravating this condition is the intense independence of both cultures which was, and remains, the trait that nurtures survival. The Red Tail Hawk similarly goes where it will, eats when it wants, and fiercely guards its nest. History has shown, however, that if challenged from the outside, Seco and the Pueblo will combine for common purposes. They are as a family with coats of several colors.

Still, after at least 300 years of various forms of debate, it is not easy to stop arguing and the water issue certainly continues. However, change is certain and in recent times, renewed cooperation to develop a joint water plan that will benefit all who live from the same resource has been proceeding from negotiation to the funding stage. $2,000,000 has been raised to begin that optimistic mutual project.

The story of Arroyo Seco and its relation to the Old Church and the Outside is singular in a culture that is concerned with self-centered materialism - the characteristics that St. Francis sought to escape. In that sense, Seco is *Out of Time*. The restoration of the Old Church and its Plaza is both physical and spiritual - both of which have evolved into a new era. Barbara Waters authored an essay in the book, *Frank Waters: Man and Mystic*, in which she said that their home in Arroyo Seco was "a place of immense creative energy."[69]   She wrote, "Around us, dream and reality are one."   That description applies equally to the village of Arroyo Seco and the Old Church.

In 1998 Arroyo Seco is a real place in a real world with very real *parciantes*. While some of the challenges for survival have changed, new ones arise. The problems are still there and they are just as difficult as those that the *viejitos* faced in days that are over. Arroyo Seco can be viewed both as a Memory and a Mandate. Some might say that the Old Church is a metaphor for a community that wants to recall its roots. At the 400 year anniversary of the Oñate's conquest, it is sufficient that those of us who are new to the village and those who can claim to be part of its history, to join together. *Porque estamos juntos.*

PAZ

EL SALTO AND LUCERO PEAK

MI RAZA

By PABLO QUINTANA

They came up the Río Grande Valley
    herding their sheep, goats, and cattle
They were peaceful Basque Shepherds but
    traveled ready for battle.
They came to a wild land seeking a place
    of their own,
To raise families, their gardens and herds
    a place they could call home.
They settled at the foot of a mountain
    north, of what is now called Taos
With bricks made of mud they each
    built a fine adobe house.
These Spanish Basque the first in
    these parts
Had only their strong backs and much
    stronger hearts.
They came to live and to trade, to grow
    strong and be free.
They left Spain behind then across
    a great sea.
Their churches were closed. The padres
    returned back to their homes.
These people got together and built a
    strong faith of their own.
They built the moradas, their santos,
    their faith.
Took care of their own people, made
    everyone feel safe.
They died for the land, were
    determined to stay
And through all of their hardships
    they learned how to pray.
They worked hard on their ranchos
    cleaning forest and rock.
Digging acequias for miles to
    water their gardens and stock.
Some went to the mountain
    mining for the gold.

Others to gather much Leña to
     fight off the cold.
They were driven off by Indians
     but they always returned.
To the place by the mountain -the
     place they had earned.
Over three hundred years they have
     lived and have died.
Have seen lots of changes the
     tears have not dried.
Their land grants were taken divided
     and sold.
They claimed it was too much for
     one people to hold.
Today I am proud to be part of
     this Race.
At the foot of El Salto I still
     own a place,
My land is watered by the acequias they
     made.
Under trees that they planted I rest in
     their shade.
The land is now crowded, the lots
     are quite small.
I fear that someday we won't have land
     at all.
Our land taxes are raised, and
     farming don't pay.
To some folks it's already too expensive
     to stay.
They moved to the cities decided
     to run
leaving to others the work they had
     begun.
I, myself, believe it would be
     a big crime
To abandon my roots after so long a time.
     I am part of this land
Its trials and pain.
     If I had my own way
I would live it again.

ABOUT THE AUTHOR

James Bull and his wife Connie, live in Arroyo Seco and near Franktown, Colorado. Jim, a trial lawyer and past president of the Colorado Trial Lawyers Association, has published, "Frankstown, A Douglas County Crossroads" which publication supports, in part, the Frankstown Historic Museum (originally, Franktown was named Frankstown). Their family of three daughters has been active in projects involving history and historic preservation. Jim is the past president of Historic Denver, Inc. He is past president and co-founder of The Denver Firefighters' Museum and Historic Franktown, Inc. and is on the Executive Committee of the Pike's Peak Grange.

Connie, as past president of Historic Frankstown, Inc., is curator and a tour guide of the museum and is currently an officer of the Pike's Peak Grange in Franktown, Colorado. They are members of the Kit Carson Historic Foundation, the Millicent Rogers Museum, and The Taos Art Association. They have enjoyed attending services at "La Santísima Trinidad" and they love the village of Arroyo Seco, its people, and their new friends.

END NOTES

1   A "horno" is a traditional beehive shaped outdoor oven constructed with adobe brick and finished in stucco. The traditional heating
process is to build a cedar fire, which burns until a certain temperature is
achieved. The fire and coals are removed when it reaches a heat sufficient to light a piece of paper placed into the oven and away from any
fire. Bread, poultry or meat is to be placed in the oven and the door and
smoke hole are sealed with mud and burlap. Carmen Velarde of
Ranchos de Taos has instructed the author and his wife on the correct
method of using an "horno." The author persists in cooking meat in the
horno irresponsibly and without using "dry" heat. Mrs. Velarde was
responsible for building the fireplace in the Old Church in Arroyo Seco
and the Arroyo Seco morada and many other locations. Carmen who is
active in community activities lives in Ranchos de Taos. She is paints
and creates her own "retablos" of the many Saints.

2   Arroyo Seco varies from 7600 feet above sea level to approximately 8000 feet.

3   Claire Munzenrider of the Museum of New Mexico directed the
restoration of the altar screen. Volunteers applied acrylic paint permitting
corrections to be made during restoration. Wooden shims were fabricated which were inserted between the wooden panels that had separated
due to the dry air. The Arroyo Seco reredos were originally painted with
oil based colors. The other traditional method of painting used natural
pigments derived from plants and minerals. Glue used to join the wood
was produced from animal hooves that had gone through a rendering
process.

     Trudy Valerio Healy, the great granddaughter of de Gracia
Gonzales, lives nearby and has personally participated in much of the
restoration. De Gracia Gonzales lived between 1835 and 1901 and was
responsible for the carved stairway in the Molly Brown House, in Denver,
Colorado which is owned by Historic Denver, Inc. Interview with Trudy
Valerio Healy, September 25, 1998.

     A de Gracia Gonzales painting in the Regis College collection
appears in Santos and Saints, Thomas J. Steele, S. J., Ancient City Press,
Santa Fe, New Mexico, 1974 at page 85. Numerous museums including
the Millicent Rogers Museum in Taos, the Harwood Foundation, and the
Kit Carson Foundation exhibit de Gracia Gonzales work. See, Christian
Images In Hispanic New Mexico, William Wroth, The Taylor Museum,
1982. The cover of Steele's book reproduces a painting created by
Rafael Aragon (d. 1862) who carved and painted the crucifix which
hangs in the Old Church on the wall in front of the de Gracia Gonzales
reredos.

4   Article by Larry Torres, "El Crepúsculo", Taos News, August 13,
1998.

5   Interview, Palemón Martínez, November 7, 1998.

6   Archeologists might call the First People a "culture." Since the

First People are no longer a continuing and identifiable group, we have classified them "First People" rather than "First Culture" which term is applied to the to the Taos Pueblo.

7   Article by Wallace S. Broecker, "The Once and Future Climate", Natural History Magazine, September, 1996.

8   Taos News, November 16, 1995, p. A 6.

9   Article by Leslie Linthicum, Albuquerque Journal, January 24, 1998.

10   The States and Their Indian Citizens, Theodore W. Taylor, U.S.G.P. O., 1972, p. 146.

11   Various interviews with Larry Torres who served as an important consultant for this book. He has provided many of the photographs and a map of the Arroyo Seco Plaza.

12   Coronado's Land, Marc Simmons, University of New Mexico Press, 1991, Paperbound Edition, 1996, p. 47-50. Simmons states that slavery was common before the arrival of Oñate and lasted well after New Mexico and the United States abolished the practice by law.

13   The Pueblo Revolt, Robert Silverberg, Bison Press, 1970.

14   A Concise History of New Mexico, L. Bradford Prince, Torch Press, 1914, p. 117 (Prince.)   Mr. Prince was appointed a Governor of New Mexico in the late 19th century while it was still a Territory of the United States. (Prince).

15   The Pueblo Indian Revolt of 1696 and the Franciscan Missions in New Mexico, J. M. Espinosa, University of Oklahoma Press, 1988.

16   Ibid. p. 58

17   La Santísima Trinidad Parish: A Grand History, Larry Torres, Ayer Y Hoy en Taos, Taos County Historical Society, winter, 1997, p. 3. (Torres, 1997)

18   Report 90-05B. "El Torreón Del Arroyo Seco: Archeological Test Excavations at LA 80301 Near Arroyo Seco, Taos County, New Mexico," Jeffrey L. Boyer. Test excavations were conducted in the summer of 1990. (Boyer.)

19   Don Fernando de Taos was named after Don Fernando Chavez who received a land grant from the King. He returned to Taos to find his family slaughtered after the revolt of 1680 save one son. They left Taos and did not return.

20   Turmoil in New Mexico, William A. Keleher, Rydal Press, Santa Fe, New Mexico, 1952, p. 116 (f.n. 24) (Kelleher.)

21   Doniphan's Expedition, William E. Connelley, Self-Published, Topeka, Kansas, 1907, p. 516-518.

22   Padre Martinez: New Perspectives From Taos, Essay by E.A. Mares, Millicent Rogers Museum, 1988.

23   The New Mexico portion of New Spain was referred to as a "Kingdom" during the early Spanish period. Later, nearing the Mexican

period, the area become known in Spanish documents as a "province." This Miserable Kingdom, Rev. James T. Burke, Our Lady of Fatima Church, Albuquerque, New Mexico, 1973, (Third Printing) 1994. Rev. Burke is a former priest of the Holy Trinity Parish in Arroyo Seco. After Mexican Independence, New Mexico became a "Department." Under the United States, it was first a "possession", then a Territory, and finally a "State."

24   Torres, 1997, p. 3.

25   Archives Document 1297, (Spanish Archives of New Mexico), Santa Fe.

26   Case No. 01749

27   Spanish Irrigation in Taos Valley: A Study Prepared for the New Mexico State Engineer's Office, John O. Baxter, Santa Fe, N.M.1990. (Baxter).

28   Baxter, pp. 45-46.

29   Baxter, p. 48.

30   Baxter, p. 50.

31   Martínez v. Martínez, 157 P. 2d 484, 49 N. M. 83 (1945).

32   A good map of the acequia system which was used as an exhibit in water adjudication proceedings is reproduced on page 166 of the book, Acequia Culture, Water, Land, & Community in the Southwest, Jose A. Rivera, University of New Mexico Press, 1988. This book is must reading for a clear understanding of the rules relating to the acequia tradition and particularly by persons new to the area who will be acquiring water rights.

33   The Treaty of Guadaloupe Hidalgo, A Legacy of Conflict, Richard Griswold Del Castillo, University of Oklahoma Press, 1990, pp. 172-176 (Castillo).

34   Decree of the Court of Private Land Claims, Santa Fe District, November, 1892, Spanish Archives, pp. 174-176, (Doc. 503).

35   Spanish Archives, (Doc. 423).

36   To Possess The Land, Frank Waters, Sage Books, 1973. (Waters).

37   Waters, pp. 218-226. See also a shorter version of the "mystery" in, Taos Landmarks & Legends, Bill Hemp, Clarkson N. Potter, Inc., 1996, pp. 77-79. Both Hemp and Waters were local authors. Frank Waters lived in Arroyo Seco and died in 1995. Bill Hemp is active in many local organizations emphasizing history. He is also an artist.

38   Edith S.P. Manby v. Arthur R. Manby, County Court, County of Elbert, State of Colorado, Case No. 118, June 1, 1909.

39   Manby v. Voorhees, 203 Pac. 543, 27 N.M. 511 (1921).

40   Manby v. Daniel Martínez, (Case 2094, N.M. 45, Supreme Court of New Mexico, Unreported). This case was so important that it is very strange that the Supreme Court did not have it reproduced officially in

any law book. It was referred to later in Ortiz v. Suazo, 570 P. 2d 309, 91 N.M. 45 (1977). The Ortiz case is interesting because it details some of the history of the unreported earlier case.

41   Baxter, p. 51

42   Baxter, p. 51.

43   In 1970 the Taos Pueblo overcame conservationist opposition to securing the return of the sacred "Blue Lake" and the surrounding lands. They were opposed by their own senior U.S. Senator, Senator Henry Jackson, who chaired the Senate Interior Committee in achieving this victory. President Nixon and the Department of Interior supported the Pueblo in its quest to pass P.S. 91-550, December 15, 1970, (84 Stat. 1437). The States and Their Indian Citizens, Theodore W. Taylor, U.S. Department of the Interior, Bureau of Indian Affairs, 1972, p. 156.

44   Boyer's work referenced in footnote 18, infra, combined a number of archeological measuring techniques including the analysis of lithic and surface material. The research showed that the area had been occupied by various groups including pre-Hispanic people. Because the site has been reduced to rubble, it is difficult to precisely establish a date. Therefore a range is used. Foundations were found indicating the location of the tower complex and other appurtenant uses. For purposes of this discussion it is sufficient that the site evidences Hispanic use in the mid 18th century or 250 + years from today's date.

45   Keleher, pp. 61-104.

46   Interview, Nancy Quintana Carrasco.

47   Forgotten People, George I. Sánchez, (Sánchez) University of New Mexico Press, 1940.   The author, a Taos native, wrote that 93% of Taos County was of Spanish descent in 1936 (p. 30) and it had the second lowest school budget in New Mexico in 1938. (p.72). He was highly complimentary of the educational delivery systems despite the meager funding and notes that most teachers were bilingual.

48   Ski Pioneer, Ernie Blake, His Friends and the Making of Taos Ski Valley, Rick Richards, Dry Gulch Publishing, 1992.

49   Ghost Towns & Mining Camps of New Mexico, James E. and Barbara Sherman, University of Oklahoma Press, 1975, p. 7. (Sherman).

50   Sherman, p. 210.

51   Grant, pp. 9-12.

52   Brothers of Light, Brothers of Blood, Marta Weigle, Ancient City Press, 1976, p. 22-23. (Weigle).

53   The term "anglo" is ". . . applied loosely to any white European mixture, particularly an English-speaking white person coming into this area from the eastern and middle western states." A Dictionary of New Mexico and Southern Colorado Spanish, Ruben Cobos, Museum of New Mexico Press, 1983, p. 111. This writer has noted that in his experience the term means "stranger" or "non-Hispanic" and it is not necessarily derogatory unless specific slang precedes the word. Those slang words

are fairly easy to discern.

54   Taos News, Larry Torres, February 27, 1997.

55   Weigle, pp. 211-216.

56   The Penitente Order has had a huge impact on the history of Northern New Mexico and Southern Colorado. Because it is a "secret" society, its workings not only are not understood but often misunderstood. It has had a mixed history and was associated with non-mainstream religious customs which were condemned by the Archdiocese in New Mexico and are no longer observed. Today the active moradas still play an important religious and social role in Hispanic society. Any summary of their activities does disservice to this fraternity. The San Luis Cultural Center in southern Colorado maintains an instructional display of a morada. Even the exact origin of the Order is not an agreed historical fact. Many authorities believe it was an outgrowth of the Third Order of Saint Francis which was a lay religious Order. The Penitentes of the Sangre de Cristos, Bill Tate, Tate Gallery, 1966. Weigle, pp. 27-37.

57   Rio del Norte, Carroll L. Riley, University of Utah Press, 1995, p. 244.

58   Spanish and Mexican Land Grants and the Law, Edited by Malcolm Ebright, Journal of the West, Sunflower, University Press, 1989, p. 4.

59   Prince, p. 191.

60   Keleher, p. 349.

61   Interview, Jessica Gutiérrez, Taos County Planning Department, March 16, 1998.

62   Interview with Pablo Quintana, 1998.

63   Undated letter of Frank Waters to Taos Land Trust.

64   Taos Land Trust Newsletter, summer, 1998.

65   Interview with Palemón Martínez, January 19, 1997, and December 6, 1996. Mr. Martínez has served on the Acequia Commission for more than 30 years. He has chaired the efforts to establish an earlier water priority date for the village. His family dates to the founding of Arroyo Seco. He was the Chairman of "La Santísima Trinidad" Restoration Committee, currently raises cattle in the area and serves on numerous boards and associations dedicated to preservation of the culture.

66   Interview with Fermín and Irene Torres, December 5, 1995. Mr. Torres Father, O.V. Torres migrated into Arroyo Seco from Los Animas, Colorado. The family is original to the "Kingdom" of New Spain and recently celebrated its 400th anniversary in the area.   Luís Torres is Fermín's brother. Mr. Luís Torres and his family have also resided on El Salto Road in the original family ranch. They raise Charolais cattle. All of the children of the Torres families who live in the Arroyo Seco area are extremely active in its agricultural, religious, educational, cultural and historical affairs. There are so many active Torres family members that it

was impossible to talk to all of them in preparation for this book with the time constraints imposed on publication

67   Interview with Palemón Martínez, January 12, 1997.

68   Current statistics supplied by the Taos County Chamber of Commerce in its Fall, 1998, Membership Directory and Profile publication at page 7 report that there are approximately 2119 residents of the Taos Pueblo of the 26,634 person population of Taos county. Of 1,444,480 acres in the County, 4.3% are "Native American land. 50% of the land is federally controlled, 6.7% is state owned and 38.2% is privately owned. Ethnic composition is 65 % Hispanic, 27% Anglo, 7% Native American and 1% other. The population statistics were compiled from 1990 Census Data and Sunwest Bank.

69   Frank Waters: Man & Mystic, edited by Vine Deloria, Jr., The Frank Waters Foundation, 1993, p. 77.

70   Photographs in this book by Terry Wolff may be seen in color on the World Wide Web at www.taoswolf.com/taosalbum and note cards are available. More information about Arroyo Seco, New Mexico can be found at www.taoswolf.com/seco and Trinity Parish at www.taowolf.com/trinity.

71   Copies of this book may be purchased from Wolff Publishing Works at www.taoswolf.com/wolffpub/time.

LA SANTÍSIMA TRINIDAD CHURCH
Circa 1834, Renovated 1998
Photograph by Terry Wolff